M000107148

2

$3
1.50

TORTURED BY SOUND

BEYOND HUMAN ENDURANCE

TORTURED BY SOUND

BEYOND HUMAN ENDURANCE

Angeline:
Best Wishes,
Carol Brook

Carol Lee Brook

Roaring Productions, Inc.

CALIFORNIA

Copyright © 1999 by Carol Lee Brook

All rights reserved. This is a true story. Only a few of the names have been changed in the interest of privacy. Except for brief quotes used in reviews, no part of this book may be reproduced by any means without the written permission of the publisher.

Roaring Productions, Inc.
1318 High Street
Alameda, CA 94501

Printed in the United States of America

ISBN: 0-9664620-0-9
LC: 98-93844

Dedicated to
Dr. Pawel J. Jastreboff
and
For those who suffer . . .
For those who've died

The intent of this story is solely to help people.

In Memory of
My parents—Betty and Nat Gillette,
My brother—Chuck Gillette, and
My dear, dear friend—Celia Ness

. . . But I have promises to keep,
And miles to go before I sleep . . .

—Robert Frost
1874-1963

Acknowledgments

You stayed with me, Fred. For that I will always be grateful. You alone are the reason I survived long enough to reach Dr. Jastreboff. All my love to you. Your immeasurable patience, help, and untiring support for this project have made it possible.

The "I love you, Mom's," from our son, David, made living a necessity.

To those who came into my life and into my story, I thank you forever—I love you, too! My gratitude to these special people: Lizbeth Hasse, my attorney; Deborah Cady; Roberta Tennant; Ken Debono; Greg Benson; Flo Selfman; and Julie Segedy.

My story says everything I feel about Dr. Pawel J. Jastreboff. He and his beautiful family are always in my thoughts. I am honored to be able to tell the world about him. I am so blessed to be alive.

Suddenly, Carol hears a high-pitched shrieking noise. She looks up at the lights.

"Isn't that sound terrible?"

"What sound?"

"That horrible noise!"

"What noise?" Fear grips her heart. Sweat pours down her body. No one else hears it!

TORTURED BY SOUND

BEYOND HUMAN ENDURANCE

Prologue

1989 NEW YORK CITY

Carol holds the receiver as far away as the cord will stretch. Fred is screaming into the mouthpiece clear across the United States. "Don't you think thirty-five days in Europe is enough? Now another side trip? You're taking advantage!"

My husband is always so liberal. Could he be jealous? No. That's silly! He has nothing to be jealous about. Fernando is just my dear friend and soon-to-be boss. That's all!

Then Fred says what's really on his mind. "Everyone in my office is talking about you running all over the world with another man!"

How can she tell her husband that even though she still loves him, she cares for this other man, too? How can she make him understand that this is a different kind of feeling, a friendship, nothing more?

Fernando is waving the tickets while she's on the phone in New York. It's only a few days' detour to Bermuda. Carol listens to her heart and goes with him.

The island looks deserted. They are in the boondocks. Then comes the crash. In one split second, they are hurled into the air as their taxicab is rear-ended by a drunken truck driver. Fernando and Carol are in an ambulance on their way to the hospital. Carol is on her way to a world where reality no longer exists!

OCTOBER 13, 1993 SAN LEANDRO, CALIFORNIA

Carol deliberately leaves the back door to her house unlocked as she goes outside. She never does this. She instinctively knows that she needs a quick entry inside, away from something. But what?

This just doesn't happen. It can't! Am I imagining it? It isn't humanly possible! She has to dismiss it, and yet. . . . *I know I just heard the overhead electrical wires vibrating. No! I must be mistaken. On the other hand, I could actually hear the current running through the wires!*

She glances again toward the black sky. She looks at the telephone poles. Everything appears normal. The noise is gone. *I imagined it! No, I didn't!* Something weird is going on with her eyes, but what's this other peculiarity?

She races excitedly into the living room. "Fred, I just heard the electricity running through the telephone wires. Fred, did you hear what I said?"

Fred laughs. He's making fun of her. No, he isn't. He's laughing at his favorite television program, *Jeopardy.*

Carol looks down at Peanut. She knows that if dogs could understand and speak, hers would say, "Wow! No kidding?" Peanut would believe her!

Something unnatural has just occurred outside her house. It seems futile to think about it. It's too bizarre. She just wants it to go away!

She can't see it, and she doesn't want to experience it again. She knows no one on earth will ever believe her. She is soon to be proven right. What she doesn't know is that the thing that is manifesting itself like a strange phenomenon *is* real. If only Carol had been listened to . . . if only she had been believed. . . .

Something has been off kilter with her for years. She doesn't understand it. She can't define it. Now, whatever it is, it has just shown itself again. She doesn't believe in ghosts or in the supernatural, but this thing must be closely related.

She knew from the beginning that she would follow Fernando into eternity. She feels as if she is locked into an afterlife with him now, a surreal experience. She is playing out a drama unknown to the human race. There is no turning back. It is too late!

Carol recalls the exact time and place where they met. Is life a game with cards that you play? You draw one chance encounter. It turns out to be death in disguise. Avoid like the plague, the card should warn.

It's all just for fun at the time, a harmless, innocent game. Had it occurred because of the fashions or because of his magnetic looks?

If only she hadn't gone on that bus ride with her mother. Why had her phobia of flying in a helicopter with Fred over an Alaskan glacier brought her to a condition more frightening than death? Was this supposed to happen for a reason?

It all began so very long ago. . . .

SEPTEMBER 1986 SKAGWAY, ALASKA

Carol stretches lazily on the uncomfortable bed in the cubbyhole-size room. She peers out the window. "Gosh! Look at that glacier."

It's funny how one experience is a catalyst for another. Here they are cruising in Alaska. All because Fred felt cheated out of their Japanese Exposition trip two years ago. Not one of the exhibits was in English. But after all, wasn't everything in Japan supposed to be spoken in Japanese? Otherwise, Fred would never have thought of arranging this wonderful cruise package to the Canadian Expo. Carol's fate seems to be predestined. She rubs her tired eyes.

She compares the walking space of the cabin with the square footage of the trailers she lived in during her early school years. The money that was not present then was insignificant compared to the abundance of love showered upon both her and her brother by their parents.

Always used to plenty of attention, Carol was fascinated right from the start with her husband's nonchalant demeanor. Now her eyes follow him around the cabin of the ship while she hears him speak at that noisy party almost twenty years ago.

"Hi. I saw you come in. Would you like me to get you a drink? My name is Fred. I thought maybe you'd like to join me at a table over there. I just returned from a camping trip. I have pictures with me of the burros we rented."

Who is he? Is he for real? Donkeys at a cocktail party? *Carol sits at Fred's table. The animals she views in his pictures had gone astray. They ran off with all the supplies. This young man in front of her and his hiking party were left totally deserted. They were alone in the middle of a canyon. Is she not supposed to laugh?* He seems like fun. Does he like me? Or just the animals with the big ears?

"I'm so glad I'm not going on that horrible helicopter ride, Fred."

"Just have fun on the bus trip. Try to be patient with your mother. She's not getting any younger, you know. I'm going down for breakfast." He kisses her good-bye.

Betty, Carol's mom, wants to be with her daughter constantly. She is a widow. She is lonely. Carol loves her mom, but can't seem to make her happy. No matter how hard she tries, she always fails. She has often asked her mother to come live with her and Fred. Betty keeps refusing.

Fred has Helen, their old family friend, and her sister Grace to keep him company on this particular day. The two women are close to her mom's age. They have known each other for years. They travel together frequently, except today. Carol skips the scary helicopter ride. She peers out the cabin window again. It looks freezing, so she dresses warmly.

Carol knows her mother doesn't care in the least about taking this bus trip through the Yukon. Betty just wants to be with her daughter. At home, Carol visits or takes her someplace almost every day. Now she and Fred are taking her on every trip they make. Carol still feels like her mom thinks she doesn't spend enough time with her. Carol sure hopes Betty can see the scenic beauty around them instead of missing her conveniences in her condo.

Carol knocks on the cabin next door. Helen scurries past, looking exasperated, like she's annoyed with Betty, with whom she is sharing the room. She waves a "see-you-later" gesture. Carol begins to dread what lies ahead.

"Let's go, Mom! We're never going to get a seat on that bus unless we hurry up." Already she's impatient with her mother, and Betty hasn't even done anything—yet.

They make their way to the back of the bus. Now they're going to have to sit in the last row. It doesn't matter, though. Carol has such miraculous, acute hearing. She can sit anyplace and hear perfectly. Carol finds two seats in the same row on opposite sides of the aisle.

"All I did was move that curtain aside." Carol looks across at her mother.

Is this why Helen seemed annoyed?

"Can you imagine? She put it right back. But I fooled her and did it again when she went out of the room."

"Mom, what are you talking about? Let's pay attention to the bus driver narrating this trip. Try to forget whatever happened. It's so minor!"

Betty doesn't listen to her daughter. She continues on. Then. . . .

"Carol, I think you love Helen better than your own mom! You'll be glad when I'm dead and gone and then you won't have to bother with me anymore!"

"How can you say that?" Carol's feelings are hurt, but she promises to be patient today. Until. . . .

"Did you hear, Carol, what the driver just said?"

"Yes. I heard him. They're having moose meat stew for lunch, with local entertainment serenading us."

"I'm not going to eat moose meat. I'd rather starve!" Betty screams out while moose meat lovers look on.

Carol hears the driver announce a long-awaited rest stop. *Thank God! I'm saved!* She immediately grabs her old, unfashionable, London Fog jacket lined with fake fur for warmth. She wears comfortable jeans, nothing to rave about, nothing stylish. Her shoes are one step up from her mother's. She opts for comfort even though she has taken so many fashion courses that she's lost count. She is conscious that her handmade, bright red, mohair cardigan sweater, with the extra wide collar and zippered front, is getting stares as she works her way to the front door of the bus to escape. She always enjoys receiving compliments on her creations. She usually giggles and shrugs them off with a simple "Thank you."

Now the rest stop is over. Carol re-enters the bus.

I don't want to put up with this! There has to be another seat away from my mother, and I'm going to find it! She stops to stare at the beautiful earrings on a woman in the front row.

"Lady, will you please sit down!" the bus driver fumes.

"Can I sit here?" She points to the step.

"I'll lose my license. You'll have to take a seat."

"Are you using this one behind you?" Carol points again. "Are these your things?" Multiple cameras are stacked precariously high.

"No. They're not! That seat's available," the driver answers angrily.

This sure beats the back of the bus and my mother. "Is this your stuff?" Carol directs her question to a fellow sleeping in the aisle seat directly opposite the woman wearing the pretty jewelry.

The fellow doesn't answer. Carol gives him a little foot kick to get his attention. "Is this seat taken?" she repeats.

He looks up. Does he speak English? she wonders. He blatantly surveys her appearance. *If I meet his requirements, maybe he'll give me the seat.* He looks perturbed. Very slowly, he removes one piece of camera equipment at a time, placing each underneath his seat. Finally, the seat is empty. Carol collapses.

"My mother is driving me crazy in the back of the bus. My husband and two lady friends are crashing into a glacier right about now, and my son is on a sinking boat in the San Francisco Bay instead of studying for his UC Berkeley exams, which he will probably flunk."

She's winded. She hasn't inhaled. He smiles and stifles a laugh. "Hi. My name is Fernando." He makes no comment on her family dissertation.

She looks into the darkest brown eyes she has ever seen. They appear to be laughing at her. Fernando is handsome, with jet-black hair hanging over his forehead. He's really cute! She's lucky to have found this seat away from her mother.

"I love your sweater," he says, right off the bat.

"Thanks."

"Did you make it?"

"Yes."

"Can you take it off? I'd like to look at it better."

Is this guy coming on to me? She removes the sweater and hands it to him. He seems really impressed with her handiwork. Carol proceeds to describe in detail how she designed and constructed her project. She wonders why her sweater is of interest to this foreign stranger. He tells her that he is from Guadalajara.

The two of them laugh and talk as if they'd been friends all their lives. Suddenly she sees her mother weaving her way down the aisle of the bus with an expression that is far from friendly. It is at this very moment that any notion of going back to her former seat is banished from Carol's mind. There Betty stands, hands on hips. Carol wonders if her mother knows that she forgot to take her belongings with her, leaving them with the thieves at the back of the bus.

"Aren't you ashamed? You have a husband on this trip! Everyone on the bus can hear you laughing and talking!" Betty waits for no response. Instead she struts to the back of the bus, leaving Carol to face the stares from the passengers as her face turns beet red.

Fernando laughs, and Carol suddenly feels better. They begin to talk again as if nothing has happened. They are from different worlds, but their lives will become entangled forever.

How could Carol possibly know that Fernando is a prominent fashion designer and that his family owns a very large manufacturing business? She's certainly making a fool of herself explaining a craft he knows so well. How could she realize that her future will hold a long, close, personal relationship with this man and his family—that she will have a career in the fashion world, attend all the Paris fashion shows, ski the Alps and many resorts in the United States, travel halfway around the world as a result of this one chance encounter . . . and that fate will take her into a hellish nightmare, where sound will become her enemy and death will become her friend.

Chapter 1

OCTOBER 14, 1993

Carol awakens tired and hobbles to the bathroom. She turns on the light, squinting from the brightness, and examines her swollen eyes in the mirror. Her thoughts go to her local internist who has been so unfeeling about a condition that is rapidly undoing her nerves. Her red eyes are not only inflamed looking, but also very itchy and burning severely. Goopy stuff keeps dripping down her face.

Is this a doctor she should keep for future problems? Does her now-deceased parents' doctor really lack empathy for illness? Doctors are supposed to be sympathetic with suffering. At least he finally gave Carol the pills that she told him had helped her in the past.

She remembers her favorite doctor from two decades ago. *"You have blood poisoning, Carol. Don't go in chlorine water with a spandex bathing suit."*

"Can I die if I do?"

"Yes!"

She can never forget and will never disobey his instructions. Is this eye malady related to a chlorine mishap after all these years?

Her internist's obvious annoyance had surprised her. Did she act that badly in his office? She had made up for it. She had knit his wife a baby blanket in her favorite color. She'll stick with him a little longer.

"**P**ea-nut! Where is that little monster?"

Carol begins a routine search for her black four-pound Yorkshire darling. She checks under the king-size bed on which Fred lies asleep, breathing heavily. She tiptoes quietly through the rest of the house trying to find her dog.

"Darn these eyes." She once again stops in the bathroom to look in the mirror. She tries to convince herself that they are beginning to heal.

The mirror reflects a woman who defies her advancing age. Carol appears a lot younger than she is. She fusses with the hairdo that she has recently let grow long. She wears it professionally curled in the latest Bo Derek style.

She can still smell the fumes from her recent permanent. Her mother's philosophy that she would damage her hair with chemicals haunts her this morning. The infected eyes stare back at her. *Did my perm cause this? I love my new hairdo, but in no way was my curly 'do worth this.*

At her recent high school reunion, her friends had said that she really hadn't changed. She still feels like that silly teenager she had once been so very long ago.

She again thinks of her mother. "What do you need all that goop on your hair for?" It's almost as if she's speaking from the grave. "You look pretty without all that stuff!"

Carol smiles into the mirror. Both her parents had instilled the utmost confidence in her. She is capable of doing whatever she wants and is positive she will succeed at whatever she attempts.

Her girlfriends envy her figure. Her husband teases her over the large quantities of food she can consume without her five-foot-four inch, 115-pound frame gaining an ounce. Her father used to call her "Sunshine" but her mother used to admonish her for giggling over everything. "Life is serious, Carol," she would say.

She stares into the mirror, wondering if her silly ways are a protection, a means to handle all the tragedies she has been forced to bear. Her mother's illness still does not seem believable. Her severe stroke had caused brain damage. She had been mute for a year and a half before her death. Carol thinks of her own good health and energy as a gift bestowed upon her for trying to have kind, caring ways.

"There she is!" She bends over and scoops up the bony little body of the animal she so adores. "My little sweetheart! Mommy loves you so." Peanut automatically lifts one leg first and then the other. She obediently gets into one of the many hand-knit sweaters labeled "Made by Carol" that she's being forced to wear. Peanut has helped her live through all kinds of grief. She is a source of happiness and contentment in Carol's life. She would die before giving up her precious, adorable dog, even though Peanut is an annoyance to Fred and the neighbors with her constant woofing at the drop of a hat.

"Why is Peanut barking like that?" Fred looks half asleep as he comes into the kitchen.

"She's excited. She thinks she's going with me. I promised Bernice I'd help her pick out some glassware at Macy's."

"Do you have to do it so noisily? I'm going back to bed."

To Carol, this is just another uneventful, normal day. Fred is complaining as usual about Peanut's barking. Carol's up and about emptying the dishwasher and taking care of her dog. However, she is unaware that soon she will be embarking on a journey that will take her into a world where life has no meaning. In this other world, she will not be able to return to the past nor escape from the future. She will be stuck in a point in time. No one will believe her. She will not understand what is happening, and she will be all alone.

"**O**h, Peanut! Why did I tell Bernice I would go with her?" Carol talks to her little dog as they trudge up the block. "Your mommy just never has enough hours in the day. She is so tired from this horrible eye ordeal and our Mexico stay." She looks down at her favorite companion and smiles. Of course Peanut understands what she's saying. Peanut had stayed in Guadalajara with her, hadn't she?

Carol had studied advanced Spanish at the Autonoma University all summer. Peanut had been her companion. This brave little dog had weathered cockroaches, heat, and even thunderstorms in a secluded house on the edge of campus. She's a little doll. Carol never regrets taking her anyplace. She has carried canine equipment all over the world. She's really proud of herself. She takes such good care of the two of them, even so far from home. Other visitors get sick from food and water in Mexico. Not them. Carol walks quickly. Peanut needs breakfast.

Carol grieves for Fernando. She misses him. She was overwhelmed by his sudden death. To try to ease the pain from her loss, she bought her priceless pet. Then she had set up her deceased Mexican friend's brother, Roberto, with one of the largest fashion houses in the United States. No, there isn't anything she can't solve or handle.

"**B**ernice is here, Fred. I'm leaving. Here's a kiss good-bye." Carol bends over her drowsy husband.

"Have a good time." He kisses her back.

"Yeah, some good time. Already she is annoying me. Does she have to keep honking? I hear her! The whole neighborhood can hear her."

Carol watches her already nervous, hyped-up friend maneuver the car into heavy traffic.

"Wouldn't you know it? Look how long it's going to take us because of this awful construction," Bernice laments.

Carol wonders what she was thinking when she agreed to accompany Bernice. The construction and freeway noises seem extra loud today. Bernice's car engine seems to be extra noisy, too.

Upon entering Macy's, Bernice says, "Let's not look at anything but the glasses."

Carol resentfully accompanies her friend to the glassware department. She sees a chair and sits down.

"Bernice, I'm right here," she calls out. Bernice is already being bossy and domineering. But Carol thinks of her as the big sister she always wanted. She knows Bernice has her best interests at heart. *Why did I come today? I have so much to take care of at home.*

"Aren't you going to help me find a gift?"

"No! Come over and get me when you find something. I'm tired!" Carol knows darn well that her friend will get whatever she wants, regardless of her opinion.

Bernice plows through the wares like an animal searching for its prey.

Suddenly, Carol is startled by a blaring, high-pitched squeal. It drills through her head. She glances up at the ceiling. She stares at the fluorescent lights, aghast! Sweat pours down her body. Bernice is waving across the room.

Carol drags herself over to her friend. "I don't feel good!"

"What do you mean?"

"Isn't that terrible?" she asks.

"What?" Bernice wants to know.

"That horrible noise!"

"What noise?"

It is at this very moment that Carol knows she is in deep trouble. The fact that she is the only one hearing the noise is more than she can bear.

"Bernice! You have to take me home right now!"

"Go sit down! I won't be long. I need to get my gift wrapped."

"No! I have to leave now, this very minute! I'm sick!"

Bernice is startled by Carol's unusual outburst. "You can't be that bad off. I want to look for a minute in the purse department. It's right by the exit."

Carol hangs onto the ledge of the purse counter. *I am that bad off, Bernice. Nobody should know how bad off I am!*

"Thanks for driving me home. Sorry I ruined your day." Carol races into the house and collapses on the bed.

She has recently endured the horrendous illness and death of her mother and her designer friend from Mexico. What's one noise compared to all that? But then the high-pitched squeal is one heck of a noise. It sounds like her deceased father's electric saw. Nevertheless, she decides to weather the storm and not say anything to Fred. *It will go away. It has to!*

Chapter 2

Fred has already taken Carol the week before to a major medical center in San Francisco. She has seen a renowned skin specialist to discover if there is a connection between her past swimming pool illness and her recent mysterious eye disorder. This allergic reaction twenty years ago has been the only serious illness in her entire life.

Now Fred is taking her to a chemical ophthalmologist to further alleviate her worries.

"I have to go back to the car, Carol. I forgot something." Carol stands on the sidewalk, shaking with fear. "You go on ahead, or you'll be late for your eye appointment. I'll meet you there," Fred says, as he turns around and starts to leave.

"Fred, no. I need you to stay with me!" The street seems to be doing something. But what? Why all of a sudden is she afraid to walk alone on the sidewalk?

Inside the doctor's office, the ophthalmologist says, "Your eyes appear fine. Whatever was there is gone."

"But I hear this noise. Do you know what it is?"

"I don't know anything about noises," the nice eye doctor admits.

There has to be a connection. Carol tries to act normal, but something is possessing her entire being. An evil force? Whatever it is, it looks like it's here to stay.

The following day, Carol decides to see an ear specialist. The high-pitched tone has been constant since she first heard it in Macy's.

"Where's my old doctor?" she asks the obvious replacement who is writing on a chart. Without waiting for his answer, she continues, "He's the one who told me that I have ear pain from neuralgia."

"He sold me his practice. I have your file, if you would like to continue here." The doctor motions for her to enter his examining room. "Now what can I do for you today?"

"I hear this God-awful high-pitched squealing tone in my right ear."

Carol notices a half grin on his face. She hears a chuckle as he replies impersonally, "You have what is called 'tinnitus.'" He checks her ears with his instrument. "Your ears look fine."

"Tinnitus? What's that? How do I get rid of it?"

"It's a common ear noise that millions of people hear in one way or another. You can't make it go away, but sometimes it'll stop by itself." She starts to cry. How did she get this? Why does this doctor think it's funny? She sure doesn't! The doctor leaves his patient sitting, dabbing at her eyes. *What's going to happen to me?*

Carol will not recall for some time her deep foreboding about a bumper sticker she read on a car less than a week before: "Tinnitus Knows No Silence." She thought at the time, "Dear God. How horrible!" Now she feels frightened as she reads and rereads the saying in her mind. Why would anyone place such a sticker on their vehicle? She had taken the sign personally even before her "sound" began.

She had gone to Calistoga, her favorite health resort, with Helen. She was deliberately staying away during Peanut's knee operation. She was trying not to be upset over her dog's surgery by swimming and laughing. Coming home late at night, her car had made a scraping noise. In the morning, the noise was gone. What was that all about, she wondered. Then she had seen the bumper sticker. She doesn't believe in premonitions and omens, but this sure is one she will come to believe.

F̲red enters their bedroom and finds Carol sprawled out on the bed.

"I have tickets for a catered dinner on a chartered boat. Do you want to go?"

"Yes." It sounds like fun. Fred lacks the ability to be empathetic with serious problems. He is honest and forthright though. He is devoted to the son they have raised. Carol and Fred have a business together. Marriage is an even greater commitment. Carol's mother had often said, "Fred's other good qualities are more than enough to compensate." On the other hand, he hasn't been much support for Carol emotionally through her past crises when her parents were dying. God knows how he's going to act now!

She awakens the next morning with a stabbing pain in the ear that has just been examined. She also hears banging noises. The high-pitched tone appears to be gone. *Thank God at least the electric drill has stopped!* She decides to tell Fred what she has been going through.

"Fred! I'm hearing booming noises coming out of my ear!" She starts to cry.

"Does this mean you're not going to my boat function?"

She looks at her husband hatefully. He is so difficult to live with because of his changing emotional makeup. But this response?

He bends over and kisses her good-bye. "Have a nice day."

She lies on the bed sobbing. She reaches for her Allergen eardrops that she thinks of as her miracle pain killer. Why aren't they working? She swallows Tylenol. She can't tell which is worse, the stabs of pain or the banging noises. She lies crying. At this point, she doesn't know what extreme terror or anxiety is. She is sure that whatever she has can be fixed.

She needs a doctor! The only one Carol knows, she has come to despise. He made light of her dysfunctional eye condition. She calls him anyway.

"I was hearing a high-pitched sound screeching very loudly. Now it's changed to thumping noises with a lot of ear pain."

"I see. I'll call in a prescription, and you take it as directed."

"What're you giving me? Will it make the noises go away?"

"Maybe. Actually it's a sedative to calm you down."

For ear pain? That evening . . . "Fred, the doctor prescribed a sedative for my ear. Can you imagine?" Her eyes start to tear.

"I think that's a wonderful idea. It'll make everything fine for you again." Carol is shocked. She is furious at receiving the same nonfeeling reaction from her husband as from her doctor.

Something is definitely happening. It seems more apparent in some surroundings than in others. Carol starts to have diarrhea from terror and extreme anxiety. Oddly, she feels the need to stuff her ears with cotton, and she strangely feels better from doing so.

That evening, walking to the boat, Carol says, "I feel sick, Fred."

"You'll feel better after you see this gorgeous boat and eat something."

How much more can I endure? She is trying to please her husband, but she is beginning to see him as an unfeeling monster. She watches him gulp down all the luscious-looking dishes that she normally would be eating. Her nerves are getting the best of her. She screams, "I'm sick! I want to go home right now!" The yacht people are staring.

"I just want to have dessert first," Fred firmly states.

Carol collapses on a chair. She prays that she won't pass out from the stabbing pain and thumping noises. She looks at her husband, wishing that the yacht were in the middle of the bay instead of docked. She'd like to push him into the depths of the water to watch him drown, like she knows *she* is doing.

Carol awakens the next morning, touches her ear, and listens for the earth-shattering noise. "Yea! It's gone!" Everything seems to have disappeared. She awakens Fred with the good news.

"That's nice," he says.

"I'll still go in for the sinus x-ray. I made an appointment with a new doctor. I may have caught Bernice's infection." Carol doesn't quite know what a sinus infection is, but it sounds like a feasible explanation for the ear pain and noises.

The medical building seems strange during the x-rays. Something is wrong and altered. Something has invaded her body. She can't wait to get home.

Instead, Carol stops her car at a neighbor's house. She runs up the stairs and knocks loudly. "Is anyone home?" She sits on the doorstep and wipes her tear-filled eyes. She hears clicking noises like sharp bursts of sound. *Are we going to have an earthquake?*

Carol has extraordinary "Wonder Woman" hearing. She has the capability to hear things others cannot. She's aware of planes approaching from miles away. She sits, trying to determine just what it is she is experiencing. Suddenly, she is afraid to enter her house.

Everyone says that nothing is wrong. Why aren't her x-rays positive?

The next day, after a sleepless night, Carol is again horrified. She doesn't have the foggiest notion as to what's happening. Without warning, she hears four distinct loud booms—**boom boom boom boom**—one right after the other. A drum roll immediately follows. She is terrified! She phones Fred's CPA office. Why?

Mary Ann, his secretary, tells her that he has gone to the bank and should be back in about thirty minutes.

Thirty minutes! I'll never make it! She immediately dials Bernice. "Can you come right over? I need help!"

When her friend arrives, Carol tells her what is happening. "I hear booming noises. They keep repeating over and over—**boom boom boom boom!** Then a wind-up noise—**rrrrrrrrrrr.** There are four really loud sonic-type booms." Bernice looks funny. Carol tries to explain. "I know there are no such things as sonic booms coming out of ears, but I hear it! I really do, Bernice! What on earth is happening to me?" She starts to cry.

Bernice sits staring. She scoots to the farthest edge of Carol's king-size bed as if she's suddenly afraid of her friend. Carol sees her whole life flashing before her. Finally, after what seems like only a few minutes, Bernice says, "Well, I have to go home now and fix Willie's dinner. Fred will be here soon." The clock reads 4:45 p.m. She hears the front door close.

What kind of people have I put into my life? Dear God! When they turn to me for help and support, I'm always there for them. Now when I need stability and emotional security, they are unable to be there for me!

Carol knows that the one person she needs to lean on the most if she is to survive whatever is happening is Fred. However, she does not yet know that Fred will be her biggest adversary. She is going to have to fight him every inch of the way just to live.

"**Y**es. I'll make sure she swallows them. Yes. I understand."

Carol hears him on the phone with her internist. He seems to be plotting against her. Fred enters their bedroom, holding a glass of water.

"What's that?"

"Never mind. Just take it."

"I don't want to!"

"Come on, swallow it! Trust me. It'll make you feel better."

"What is it going to do?"

"Never mind. Just take it."

"Oh, dear God!" she cries. She is licked. She is beaten. She finally obliges and swallows Fred's pill. She knows a dose of medicine will quickly put her into a groggier state—a place where things won't seem all that important.

With each successive tablet, Carol sleeps less. She awakens and realizes what is happening. She cries out, "Fred, please help me!" She loses track of time. Her days are all the same.

Somewhere in the recesses of her constantly drugged mind, she knows that Fred is not able to help. He hasn't wanted this to happen to her, has he?

Fred has taken charge of her life, her every movement, and her seemingly progressing fears. Could he be enjoying this? Maybe it feeds his ego. She is powerless to change. She is losing choices. She has no friends to run to. Is she even able to leave?

She thinks about her good friend Helen, a woman close to the age her mom would be. No one can replace her mom. She really needs her now. Why did her mother have to die?

"Mommmmmmmm!" Her screams reverberate in vain!

"I know you'll feel better once you get out of the house," Fred says. "The music will do you good. This is the only line dancing class in our area. You went without me before to take lessons. The least you can do is go with me now. I'm going anyway, whether you come or not!"

Carol shivers with fear. The very thought of walking out the door makes her blood run cold. But the thought of staying home alone frightens her even more. She has no choice. She reluctantly agrees to go.

She feels guilty for not doing activities Fred likes. She wants to take classes with him. She loves this new dancing. She was well when she recently did it. Now it's useless to try to make Fred understand that she is too sick to dance.

In the Elks Club, Carol starts to cry. The music scares her. It roars like thunder. She sobs, "Please, Fred, take me home!"

"Go into the bathroom! Wash your face. You'll feel better in there. It'll be quieter." He continues dancing through her pleading sobs.

She tries, but the bathroom is noisy. She is alone. No one comes in. She paces back and forth crying. She covers her ears. She runs back to Fred.

"Take me home!" she demands. She doesn't care who hears.

"Go sit in the car! You're ruining this for me!"

She tries the car. The tinnitus is too loud. She races back inside. She begs Fred to leave. She cries in front of others. He doesn't care about her feelings. She hates him!

"Why can't you ever try to do what I want? You know how much I enjoy dancing!"

"I tried to wait for you in the car. It's just too noisy!"

Something physical is happening. Whatever it is, it's a total mystery. She can't figure it out, and she can't control her emotions.

At home, Carol cries, "Please go get Helen! Then take me to the emergency room! There has to be something in my ear to be hurting like this!"

Fred has asked her internist to arrange a psychiatric stay. Carol does not know about it. Fred justifies his actions with her inability to accept and cope with her condition.

In the hospital, Helen looks at "her gal" with disbelief. Carol likes Helen's affectionate reference. She looks to her older friend as a substitute mom. She tries to get feedback from her. Carol is afraid to walk down the hospital corridor alone. She fears that she will find a life-threatening force in the bathroom. She's right! The ladies' room growls like a wild beast! She believes that she has been poisoned. This is the only logical explanation.

Is she losing Helen's trust, too? Why isn't anyone coming to her aid? Why won't they believe her? And why does tinnitus make the whole world sound strange? Surely Helen will take her side. She has been Carol's friend for years. Only now Helen looks at her with amazement. She has never before seen Carol take pills.

Carol is crying in the emergency room. Helen holds her hand. Fred sits in the waiting room reading his office mail. He acts like this is a normal situation. It doesn't seem to affect him. *What's wrong with my husband?*

"Are you the doctor?" She looks up at a fellow wearing a white lab coat. He is not much older than her son.

"I'm an intern."

He listens patiently to Carol's theories. He looks into her ears. "Your ears appear clear. Stop off on your way home and get some Sudafed. Take it as directed. It should make you feel better."

Fred walks into the emergency room. He looks surprised. "Why is she staying down here?" Carol looks at Fred with contempt. The doctor looks at Fred, confused. Somebody goofed! She realizes that Fred wants the doctor to take her upstairs for psychiatric evaluation. She looks at her husband's face. It has become ugly. She hates him with all her heart!

Carol sits in McDonald's watching them. Fred and Helen are polishing off hamburgers, fries, and shakes. Evidently her ordeal has made them hungry.

After they finish eating, Fred pulls up in front of a drugstore. "Go in and get your Sudafed."

"Do you promise to wait right here?" She needs to be reassured. She is frozen with a fear she has never before experienced.

Chapter 3

There is no plausible explanation for what is happening now. The sounds have changed. Each ear has a different tone. The right side no longer has the pain and thumping noises. The heavy **boom boom boom boom** explosions with an **rrrrr** sound have been completely replaced. Now Carol hears **shoosh shoosh shoosh, hisss hisss hisss, tick tick tick tick tick tick tick tick,** all day and all night.

She knows this is real. She still has her sanity. But for how much longer?

She notices one positive thing. The intense ear pain isn't as excruciating as it was. But how on earth did the other ear get infected? If she tells Fred or anyone else what is transpiring, she will probably be carted away and put in a padded cell.

Carol is frantic! She dials an organization that one of the ear doctors has told her about, the American Tinnitus Association.

"Would you like an application to order our *Tinnitus Today* quarterly? There is a support group in your area," the voice on the phone says.

I can't believe this! Carol's hand shakes. She scribbles the name of the woman in charge of the San Francisco group.

The support person says, "There's nothing you can do for tinnitus. It may go away. It may not. In many cases, it just stops. I can test you."

Test for what? This woman says she is an audiologist. What exactly is that? I hear just fine. I hear too well. Is this all?

Carol is gripped with fear at the thought of getting into her car. Why?

Carol repeatedly dials the American Tinnitus Association throughout the coming days. She leaves messages that she is in utter agony. They direct her to an associate professor of the Neurological Surgery and Otolaryngology Department in a university back East.

The MD listens to her tale of woe. The doctor has a treatment. "Gradually build up the Klonopan from half a milligram three times a day to as high as four or even five milligrams."

This is her help? Drugs to knock Carol out of her misery. Then more drugs. No one cares that something is taking her life. A demon has possessed her body!

Carol is terrified of doing anything and everything. She forces herself to shower. The water alarms her. She is afraid to walk outside. She looks down at Peanut who lovingly waits for attention.

The refrigerator scares her. She looks it over. It appears to be the same as it always has. She and Fred chose it at the beginning of their marriage. She always loved it. Now she fears it. It's become a green monster! She won't go close to it. It must be removed at once! She dislikes her washer and dryer. They live in an alcove behind closed doors. She is glad their intrusiveness is hidden. The microwave and stove are menacing, too.

Is there anything left that I like? What's wrong with me? I can't stay alone in the house. I'm afraid!

Another local ear doctor confirms what Carol already knows. His audiologist takes a battery of tests. "You have tinnitus."

What else is new?

"Go out and ride your bike," he advises, after he learns this is what she enjoys doing.

At home, she looks at her bike. She is afraid of that, too!

Halloween is here. Carol already feels spooked. She waits until the young crowd leaves. The hissing and ticking sounds are agonizing. She shudders with fright. She has to walk Peanut. They head toward the pool.

The lampposts illuminate the darkness of the night. Carol finds no comfort in their glow. The closer she moves toward the brightness, the more her body trembles with fear. She must stay away from the light!

A car is idling. It is filled with teenagers. It's parked close to her house. She is terrified of the car. She has to keep her distance. Now she runs from a car. Her anxiety mounts. The car roar threatens. She is frightened out of her wits. The engine jumps up and down. She expects to hear it idle as usual, but it doesn't. It's louder, much louder. The kids scare her. Their voices are eerie.

She pushes the ear plugs, which she now wears constantly, in deeper. Her scream is lost in the night: "Help meeee!" She picks up Peanut and runs. There's no place to hide, and she has nobody to run to.

Someone has to be out there who can help me. Where? Where do I look? I have to find him!

Carol lives in the San Francisco metropolitan area. Surely the major medical center can advise her. She has to have someone with her. Fred doesn't want to go to any more doctors. He's convinced that she is overacting to her pain.

Why can't I make him understand that I'm not exaggerating?

Helen holds Carol's hand at the medical center where she waits to see an acclaimed ear specialist. Carol starts to sob. No one calls her in. An hour and a half later, a nasty receptionist says, "All appointments have been canceled. The doctor is going out of state. He can't see anyone else today. You'll have to reschedule."

"Come on, Carol, let's leave," Helen says.

"No! I need to talk to the doctor! And I will!"

"Get out of here right now!" the office worker orders. Carol refuses to budge. "I'll call the police if you don't leave!"

Can it be possible what I'm hearing from this unpleasant, unsociable beast? Carol stares at the woman with hate and disbelief. She no longer cares who sees her sobbing. She is in intense pain. She is suffering severely. Her condition is getting worse with every step she takes and every minute that goes by.

She runs to the pay phone outside the doctor's office to call Fred. She has to make him believe her. If she can't, she feels she will surely die!

Fred sounds sympathetic. He hears his wife sobbing hysterically. "Calm down, and drive home carefully. I've made an appointment for you with one of the best ear specialists in the world. I went to him. Do you remember? He did a brain-stem test."

Carol can't remember anything. All she can think about are the loud **tick tick ticking** noises she hears in her left ear, like her alarm clock. In the right ear, she hears **hisss hisss** and **bzzz bzzz bzzz,** like a swarm of bumble bees.

Maybe Fred does understand.

First, Carol had picked up Helen. Helen lives an hour in the opposite direction. Then she had to drive clear up the peninsula to the medical center. Now she's going to have to drive Helen all the way home—without having seen the doctor! "This is definitely unacceptable!" she exclaims.

"Where are you going?" her friend screams.

Helen watches Carol open up another door to the office they have just been tossed out of. Two men sit and laugh. One has his feet up on the desk. Is this the doctor who's leaving California in such a hurry?

"You have to help me!" she explains and then pleads. No amount of begging helps.

"I won't look in your ears. I don't know anything about symptoms of noise, pain, and poison. You should go to San Francisco General. They have a poison center there."

Carol stands sobbing. She is sick and scared. The doctor tries to get rid of her. This man is a poor excuse for a physician!

Carol sits silently next to Helen on the hour-and-a-half bus ride to San Francisco General. Is tinnitus this scary? Yes, it is! Who could feel calm with constant **hisss hisss hissing** and **sizzling**? Tinnitus is very scary!

But why is a clock-ticking sound coming out of my left ear also? Why do I have the fear of death with every changing movement of my body? Why can't I go places without dread? The bus—it sounds so strange.

Helen is looking out the window. The bus stops, lets off passengers, and moves along, as usual. To Carol, it moves to its own tune, loud and clear. It frightens her. She can't figure anything out. Tears roll down her face. Her voice whines. She cries her heart out, but she wills herself to continue on, just like the bus, until the end of the line. *What's going to happen to me, and when?*

"At least I'm not hearing **boom boom boom boom,** Helen. Surely the poison center will offer help. They have to!"

"Only you?" Carol and Helen look at the one young nurse on duty at the deserted poison clinic.

"You'll be fine. All your symptoms will go away," the nurse assures her. Carol looks at her friend for confirmation. The nurse works in the medical field. Somehow, this thought is not comforting. Carol and Helen leave.

Carol prays that the ENT specialist Fred raves about will be the correct doctor. "Someone is overlooking something important. They just have to be," she sobs to Helen, as they wait for this MD.

Helen and Fred chat. They act unworried about Carol.

The specialist tells Fred that not only does Carol have tinnitus, but he—the doctor—has it as well. She looks at the doctor who seems so cheerful and functional. *How is it possible for him to be this way if he has what I have?*

Carol tearfully says good-bye to Helen. She has a God-awful scary feeling. *The end is coming!*

Helen says, "My gal will be okay!"

She doesn't think so. *I will never be okay again! Tranquilizers can't be the only available help in the world, can they?*

Carol shares her condition and fears with her brother, Charlie. She desperately phones him in Arizona.

"Carol, I wish I were right there with you. I would put my arms around you. I would tell you that everything will be fine. You know, I shot off a gun a couple of years ago. As a result, I heard such loud air noises running through my ears that I could barely play my guitar."

"You had tinnitus?"

"Yes," he assures her. "Don't forget, mine eventually went away, and yours will, too, little sister!" Charlie's kind words and empathetic tone instantly make Carol feel better. She needs emotional support. It comes from Charlie, long distance.

Her brother is talented. He plays western music on the electric steel guitar. He has played professionally since he was a teenager. He is gifted and handsome. Johnny Cash had asked their parents' permission to take him to Nashville to play guitar with his band. "No," her parents had said. "We want him to finish high school first."

Carol can't forget Charlie's sorrow. She wishes she could go back in time. She would act differently to her brother. She would not be such a brat. Now music is her enemy, too. Everything in the world seems to be. What is it that threatens her existence?

"Oh, Charlie. Save me!" she cries, after their line disconnects.

Carol gets more desperate by the minute. Her ears must be infected. Yet why hasn't the Sudafed stopped the hissing and ticking? She lies in bed all day and all night. She keeps phoning doctors. She takes tranquilizers to survive. What caused this to happen? No ordinary doctor will ever believe her pain. Her thoughts are crystal clear. *I'm going to die! But before I do, I'm going to suffer like hell!*

Chapter 4

Carol listens carefully to the refrigerator. She visualizes it alive. It roars like a lion. The washer and dryer clang like thunder. Cars outside zoom like jets. She no longer feels safe in her home. The only solution is to find "the doctor." There has to be one special person somewhere who can treat her condition. But exactly what is her condition? Where does she look? What on earth does she have? Is it tinnitus like they say? Can it be more?

Her hands shake. She runs to the bathroom every few minutes from nerves. Her weight is dropping while her sobbing and anxiety are mounting. She is positive her ears are infected regardless of what the doctors say. Only if they are, why isn't medication helping?

She reads, "Wicks can be inserted into the ears. This allows the Eustachian tubes to open and drain." This is it! She locates an ear specialist in Oakland. He uses wicks. She'll get them at any cost. She is surprised the doctor agrees to whatever she wants. He inserts the wicks. He hands her his bill and his pills.

"Take these," the ENT wick doctor says.

More tranquilizers?

"Swallow the Xanax," the doctor and her husband say. Carol reluctantly obeys. She needs to live through the day. Neither one of them believes her.

Peanut's mommy is on the way to her grave. Carol's dog is on her way toward stardom. Peanut has a television taping in San Francisco. Carol needs to take her baby to her movie debut.

Fred and Carol approach the gate of the studio. She pushes the wicks and earplugs into place. Fred presses the admittance bell. He jumps back as if in pain from the high-pitched, shrill bell. Fred holds his hands over his ears. "How come you aren't screaming like I am from that sound if you're so bad off?"

She doesn't know how to answer Fred's outburst. She does not understand what causes her actions. Why the earplugs? She is stunned. She can't figure out which is worse, her husband or her condition. Tears roll down her face. She pulls her little dog close. Her little Peanut and son David need her the way she used to be. It's true her son is all grown up, but she has to keep thinking that he needs her. She has to ignore her husband. If she doesn't, she won't be able to endure her misery.

Fred relates Carol's behavior to their past years of marriage. Now she needs his help and financial support more than ever. She tries to overlook whatever he says. She will try to overlook his lack of feeling. She has to! She has to keep seeing doctors! She can't give up! She has to keep fighting!

The television studio is fascinating. The crew adores Peanut. She performs like a trooper. It's the human mother who can no longer perform. Why is she afraid to walk to the restroom in this interesting place? Why is she afraid to do a simple thing like that?

Carol gives up using only her medical insurance plan. Her life is at stake. She needs to act fast no matter what it costs. She calls the head nurse multiple times at the Stanford University Hearing Center. The reply is always the same: "Your tinnitus has a good chance of disappearing." Not only hasn't it disappeared, it's become worse. She still hopes to find a doctor who will cure her.

"One of the wicks fell out," Carol sobs as the first of two Stanford ENT specialists examines her ears.

"I'll remove the other wick. They are useless for you."

The second doctor comes in. "How are you doing today, young lady?"

"I am dying today, doctor." He thinks she tells a joke.

"You have number ten ears, Carol." She knows this comment is a joke.

On a scale of one to ten, I'm below a zero! But I won't be defeated. There has to be someone out there who can help me beat this. I'm going to find that "right" doctor!

Carol doesn't know why she goes back to her insensitive internist. He's useless, like her wicks and the other doctors. But she can't give up.

What does it matter anymore? One more time at the internist. One more ear specialist, or a million more. She's never going to hear anything different from them. *Why am I still trying? For my dead parents? For my husband? I guess it's for me, for my future. But do I have one? Only God knows!*

Her dog depends on her. Her dog loves her. Isn't there anyone else who does? David, her son. She's sure he loves her!

Carol goes to still another ear doctor in Oakland. *How many more will I see? When will I stop? Never! I hope I am right!*

This new one is like all the others. He looks at her skeptically. She's crazy, he's sure. He writes as she talks. He discusses antihistamines and antibiotics for therapy.

His words are meaningless. All she can hear is **hisss hisss hisss, tick tick tick.** The doctor's voice drones on. His office scares her.

Carol now sits in a neurologist's office. Nothing makes sense. Her emotional behavior has made a 180-degree turnaround. Her anxiety and fear levels reach insurmountable proportions. Sounds shoot through her ears. Everything in the world is distorted. Everything jumps up and down. Carol still has, according to all the doctors, perfect ears and hearing. So what is destroying her?

The neurologist says, "I'm sure you don't have a tumor."

"Thank God for that."

He bangs his tuning fork onto Carol's knee. He holds it close to her ear. She tells him when it resounds.

"When I ask her what she's hearing, she has to remove her earplugs before she can tell me." She hears the doubt in Fred's voice. She feels humiliated. Fred forces her to establish her sanity.

No one is ever going to believe me! She's angry! Fred thinks her condition is nothing. She hates him! If Carol has lost her credibility with her own husband, what can she expect from others?

"Go home and ride your bike," the neurologist says.

Again with the bike? Just because I list sports on their forms, I'm expected to go out and have fun?

"I'm going to take her to one of our favorite restaurants for barbecued oysters," Fred tells the neurologist.

"Good, that's very good." The neurologist looks at Carol. "This will be gone within a year. You wait and see. Next year, you won't even remember what happened. I promise you."

This doctor even promises. He has extensive medical knowledge. Why then can't she take his word? *Too bad I won't be alive next year to tell him he is wrong!*

By now, Carol has been to six ear specialists. They've all told her the same thing. No one is able to help. She can no longer smile. She only has tears and anxiety.

Fred is still his optimistic self. He alternates between kindness and bouts of rage. He has become a "househusband" without a word of complaint—taking care of the errands and chores Carol can no longer do.

I'm driving him crazy, but I can't help it! She has to get relief from her constant torture soon! But where? And from whom?

Now a minor mishap becomes a major catastrophe. She bites on a piece of shell inside an oyster. Her back tooth breaks. She can't believe what the waitress of her favorite restaurant is saying:

"I saw you using dental floss at the table. There's a ladies' room, you know. And you," she points her finger at Fred. "You were filing your fingernails, too!" *No he wasn't! He was clipping them!*

"I want both of you to leave at once! Don't ever come back!"

Carol is sorry that she reported the broken oyster shell. What's one wrecked tooth? Embarrassed, they get up to leave. Here she is, a victim of oysters. She phones the dentist for an appointment.

Carol nervously waits in the oral surgeon's office. "How much longer?" she keeps asking.

"Carol, hi. How are you?" The voice belongs to a familiar-looking face, but she is just too sick to remember whose face. She looks at the person, bewildered.

"I was in your Spanish class," the face says.

Everything is a blur as her old friend tells her how great she looks.

"I'm very sick. I've been poisoned." Tears trickle down her cheeks. The friendly face looks stunned.

Carol feels no physical pain from the surgeon's multiple injections and drilling. But she cries anyway.

"My grandmother had tinnitus," the kind oral surgeon says.

They had it in those days? It seems that many people have what she cannot live or cope with.

"**Y**ou have to get counseling!" Fred states adamantly. "When you aren't sobbing or screaming out, you're on the phone calling for help all day long and running to more doctors. This behavior has got to stop! I can't take much more of it!"

Can I? Even while he is yelling, Carol is busy making another appointment.

She thinks about this different doctor. He is listed as homeopathic. She squeezes her hands around the bottles filled with toxins. This determines what she's allergic to? She takes his shot like a puppet. There is nothing she won't allow doctors to do. There is nothing too dangerous to try. She has to rid herself of this! She will go to any lengths. But how far?

Fred thinks a psychologist is the solution. Carol knows it isn't. She is afraid to go outside. How is she to get to the psychologist?

At first, she refused tranquilizers. Now she copes better being drowsy, so she keeps increasing the dosage. She swallows drugs to deliberately knock herself out. She sleeps a small amount with them. She tries to get relief from the unbearable torture. Fred selects a "professional." Carol hears the psychologist say, "I've never heard of tinnitus. What is it?"

Strike one.

"I'm sure if I had tinnitus, I wouldn't be doing very well either."

Is this supposed to help? Maybe this is reverse psychology! Thank God I don't have a depression problem! She watches Fred pay this woman for nothing. He can't possibly want her to come back. The therapy is useless for her problems.

He says, "Thank you, we'll be back!"

Out on the street, Carol cries uncontrollably.

"Let's buy some nice groceries in this nice store," her hungry husband says.

"I can't go into that market!" How much more does Fred have to be convinced? Evidently not much!

He says, "Don't worry! I'll find you a nice psychiatrist!" And he does, too!

"I'm going to teach you how to relax. You take deep breaths," the psychiatrist says. He even gets down on the floor to demonstrate.

Is she really watching this? With all Carol's high-altitude skiing, he has to teach her how to breathe? She wonders how he would breathe while sitting on a tiny chair dangling 15,000 feet up in the Alps? She smiles as she pictures him falling. He's not doing so well in her daydream. Maybe he hasn't practiced his breathing enough.

Suddenly, Carol needs to use the restroom. She instinctively becomes afraid. She anticipates something horrible in there. She tries to control her fear, but the cold chill of death is flowing through her veins as her body grows thinner each day.

Carol looks at the adjacent door marked "Gastrointestinal." *What is a gastrointestinal? Why is the waiting room so crowded?* "I'll trade you problems," she wants to say to any of the patients.

"May I please use your bathroom?" Carol already knows that the room she is about to enter is intimidating. She's right. She is alone, sobbing and trembling. The walls close in. The evil shows its power in this confined space. It swallows her.

Chapter 5

So here she is on a plane bound for Texas—to a poison center, no less.

"What an adorable jacket! May I place it overhead?"

"Thank you." Carol sadly watches the stewardess carefully fold her coat. *What does anything matter anymore?*

A few minutes later the attractive hostess returns. "Is something wrong?"

What can she say? She has tried every seat on the plane. Should she tell her that her fear of flying has been replaced with a fear of living?

Thank God she and Bethann knew what to do. She recalls the phone conversation with her closest school friend.

"Carol, it's too coincidental. It has to be all the chemicals you put on your hair. Then with the unbalanced swimming pool water. . . ." *What, Bethann? Just what did it do?*

"I saw your eyes. This tinnitus must be a second stage. Write this doctor's name down. He happens to be local for you. If anyone will have answers, he will!"

Carol's thoughts return to the present. The stewardess is reciting the treats on her cart.

Carol automatically says, "Orange, please. Thanks." Then she realizes the probability of heartburn. "Can I change that to apple?" She takes the glass of juice and removes a brochure from her tote bag under the seat. She starts to reread the information that will save her life and make her well:

> The goal of the American Environmental Health Foundation, a nonprofit organization, is to further the practice of environmental medicine, a branch of medical science dedicated to the study and treatment of adverse environmental effects on the individual. As we damage the environment with pollutants, we risk the destruction of not only our natural resources, but of our personal health as well. Dangerous toxins carelessly deposited and introduced into our environment affect everything we come in contact with and enjoy—our food, our clothes, our homes, our workplace, and our recreational spaces.

Carol enters the Holiday Inn in Dallas. She made it through the flight! She pushes the earplugs further into her ears. Can they get stuck? She stands at the reservation counter waiting to be helped. She looks over the counter for a fax machine. She already misses Fred, David, and Peanut. She feels sick and so lonely.

Do I really hate Fred? He had driven her to the airport. His words were sincere: "Do everything they tell you, and come back to us well and happy again." *Will I?* He had tried to reassure her fearful heart. He was cheering her on when he wasn't putting her down. *Fred has always been difficult to live with. Now finally, he has a valid cause for his emotional fluctuations.*

The airport sounded unnatural. It was blaring in an inexplicable way. It would have been useless to tell Fred. Flying was the quickest mode of travel.

"You'll be staying in a special area of our hotel for patients just like you," the receptionist says, interrupting her thoughts.

There're others? Let me see them! Carol doesn't understand. Unknowingly, she is entering another world with another way of life. *I want the other me back. Everyone always thinks I'm so brave and gutsy. Now look at me!* She is already just as terrified in her new surroundings as she was in California.

On the second floor, where her room is, she uses her time well. She can't be afraid of the soft drink machine, can she? She rushes by it as quickly as possible. She tries to avoid looking directly at the red and white contraption. *It seems to be growling. It isn't doing this to the other guests. Why me?*

She runs up to the laundry machines. Then she runs down the hall away from them. She is panic stricken. She tries to figure out why the part of the hallway void of machinery is a safer area. When she gets close to the appliances, she thinks she will surely have a heart attack.

"Watch out!" says the clean laundry guest who carries a basketful of clothes.

Where did he come from? She looks back. He is picking the clothes up off the floor and putting them back into his basket.

The beverage machine is stationary. It does not follow. It does not devour. Neither do the washing machine and dryer, she notes, shaking with relief.

How am I going to take care of myself? I'm afraid of everything. I need to get on this detoxification program right away!

She thinks she might be doing things to make herself worse. This reasoning raises her anxiety along with her urgent need for help. They'll *teach me what to do at the clinic.* They *have to. That's* their *job.* She tries to console herself. *I'll do whatever* they *tell me.*

"Wait. Don't leave me! Promise you'll stay right here!"

The heavyset taxi driver looks like a Sumo wrestler. He pulls close to the entrance of the large supermarket. His cab is almost at the checkstand. He doesn't scare Carol. The market does.

Carol has come to buy yogurt. She tries to force down food. She has already shocked her nice hotel manager:

"I'm a poison victim."

"By all means then, store your grocery items in my private refrigerator."

"Don't you want to grab another taxi when you're finished?"

"No!" Carol yells back. "Absolutely not!" This scary-looking man is probably wondering why she's not afraid of him.

"Listen lady, I'll wait for you. I aim to please!" She knows the taxi driver thinks she is off her rocker. She sees him watch her race into the market. Carol grabs a novel that looks interesting. She hopes to be able to concentrate better in Texas. She has to reread everything. It's not easy to do much with **click click click click, hisss hisss hisss.**

A hotel shuttle takes her to the clinic. Carol shudders on the highway and then in the elevators. More fear seems to hit her upon entering the clinic's waiting room. She can't stop shaking. She berates herself for her fearful ways. She is determined not to cry.

"Where is all this noise coming from?" She directs her question to a kind, attractive-looking woman. The woman scoots over on the couch to make a space for Carol.

"The loud generator noises are coming from the huge fan blowers. They filter out the bad air."

Carol looks up, searching for the bad air. She becomes more frightened as the woman continues. "You can't come in here wearing leather. Your clothes will cause allergic reactions in everyone, including me!"

"Oh, my gosh! I didn't know! I'm sorry! Hi. My name is Carol."

"My name is Toni. And if you expect to get well, you had better get on with the program."

Carol is perplexed. She shakes from Toni's comments. Her body is constantly freezing. She wants to know, but is afraid to ask: "Exactly what *is* the program?"

"Where are you staying?" Toni inquires.

"At the Holiday Inn. Why? Is there something wrong with it? I was told it's fine for sick people like me."

"Well, it most certainly isn't! You better get out of there immediately and into a safe unit. Your hotel is very detrimental to you."

Oh, no! I knew it! "What do you mean? Where should I go?" Carol is horrified! She feels guilty. The hotel is comfortable. It's nice.

"I live in Rhoden Park, which is a distance out of town."

Carol's head is spinning. She immediately needs to find out everything she is doing wrong—before she gets any worse.

She learns that three doctors are treating people: an internist and surgeon, founder of the American Environmental Health Foundation (AEHF), 1975, in Dallas; another medical doctor; and an osteopath.

Carol desperately asks for Toni's phone number. She also asks for the manager's name and number of the place where Toni lives. She is grateful for this help. She is frantic to get started immediately on the program. She is relieved when she is called in to see the chief physician. Now she can start working toward her recovery.

Carol explains everything that has happened. The doctor writes as she speaks. The loud **hisss hisss hisss hisss, tick tick tick tick** resounds above her voice which she can no longer control. "Have you had tinnitus patients here before?"

"Oh, yes," he replies.

"Did they get rid of it?"

"Yes, but it takes quite a lot of treatment in the sauna."

"What about all the tranquilizers I'm taking?"

"Just stop them. Take half a milligram at night before you go to sleep."

"Is it okay to drop them all at once?"

"Yes. That's fine. What I'd like you to do now is go to the front desk and get an appointment with the nutritionist. The receptionist will also instruct you about the sauna."

"Thank you. Thank you so much!" she says to her new doctor.

Carol looks at the list of the "only" foods she is supposed to eat. She learns that anything else she ingests will make her worse.

34

The young nutritionist writes down the name of two markets in Dallas where it is permissible to breathe the air. It is mandatory that she purchase groceries and supplies in only these stores. She must avoid all other places not approved by her new establishment. This includes shopping malls. The nutritionist specifies that all food has to be organic.

Now Carol has discovered that anything that isn't organic is poisonous for tinnitus. These strict regulations only confirm her worst fears and suspicions. She has caused her own condition by what she has done and is still doing. But what is that?

"Do you want mornings or afternoons?" the young girl in the sauna room asks. The therapy room is at the end of the long and frightening hallway.

"I'll come in the morning." Carol starts reading the several sheets of instructions handed to her. Once a week she is supposed to have a doctor's appointment. Blood is to be drawn at 8:30 a.m. on that day. She can't possibly wait a whole week to get medical help. She races back to the chief physician's office.

"I want appointments with the doctor on Mondays, Wednesdays, and Fridays for the whole month." The receptionist looks surprised.

"You'll need to go to the bookkeeper each day to pay for this." The girl waits for her reaction.

Carol notices that other patients book once-a-week appointments. The additional cost has to be considered insignificant. *The main concern is to save a life—mine!*

"That'll be fine!"

Carol reads the profile for the physical therapy program. It requires wearing only 100-percent cotton clothes. It states that vital signs (weight, blood pressure, pulse, and temperature) are taken and that niacin is issued to the patient's tolerance levels. She continues to read:

35

Exercise for twenty minutes on bike, treadmill, or rowing machine. Niacin again given. Sauna for 30 minutes. Shower. Vital signs taken again. Massage done for 10 minutes. The above constitutes one session.

Normally, a patient will do three sessions per day, which takes up to four or five hours. After each session, mineral replacements are given: 1 tsp. tri-salts; 1/2 tsp. potassium chloride, 750 mg; l oz. polyunsaturated oil or 2 tsp. activated charcoal powder; and 2 tsp. pure psyllium seed 3 times per day.

This is hideous! But I'll do it anyway! I have to in order to live!

Chapter 6

Carol tries to analyze what she is seeing and reading. Her tinnitus seems to penetrate every nerve in her body. She prays that this strenuous and expensive ordeal will stop the condition that is eating her up alive. The saunas are the hottest—over 200°F—and the best quality.

She reads that some negative reactions can be abdominal discomfort, diarrhea, bloating, gas, headaches, skin eruptions, fatigue, mental confusion, mood swings, restless sleep, insomnia, irritability, urinary pain, and burning. She already has the restless sleep, insomnia, and digestive problems. Understanding this scares her even more. She has to succeed. She must ignore the negatives.

"You're in the right place. In fact, you're in the only place to cure your condition." Carol looks into a sympathetic face. The woman boosting her spirits is on her way out of the sauna. She seems to want to befriend her.

Carol wonders whether her constant crying has anything to do with this concern.

"I had a sound like a clock ticking in one of my ears. I got it from stripping a floor with chemicals. Believe me, I know how you're feeling," the stranger consoles. "I used to sit in the closet for hours hiding in the dark. I took a lot of extra vitamins and minerals during that time. I know the vitamins helped me recover. This is the only place in the world that can rid you of tinnitus."

Her words are just what Carol needs to hear. She wants to believe in what this girl is saying and in this program. Carol is so sick and has come such a long distance. When the woman says that her husband is an MD who wants to specialize in the head physician's field, Carol feels hopeful. The Environmental Health Center program has been validated and her promised recovery is reinforced. *This must be the correct treatment!*

"Would you like to walk home with me? You can see my housing. By the way, my name is Jo."

"What a cute name. I'm Carol. This is really sweet of you, but I don't know if I'm up to going." What she wants to say is, "I'm afraid to walk on the sidewalk."

"It isn't far. I usually walk every day if the weather is okay."

She's sick, too. Yet she walks on the street by herself. Carol has a chance to make a friend. Now she's ruining things right away by weeping. *No one is ever going to like me the way they used to.*

"It's okay. I know how you must be suffering." Jo hands her a tissue. Carol wipes away her tears.

They walk on the street. Carol tries to stop crying. She can't. The street howls like ferocious beasts baring their fangs. "How much further?" she asks. It's as if she and her condition are on another planet.

At the house, Carol wonders, "What's that noise running? Are you supposed to keep that on?" She looks at the barren facility. She is in the unit only a minute before her fears become overpowering. She worries about getting back to the clinic.

"They're fans that filter the air."

Carol knows that she can't endure this unit. She looks around at the meager surroundings. *Is this what I'm supposed to live in? For how long? Maybe forever?*

"See, all the furniture is made from natural materials, porcelain steel walls, and tiled floors. There is full-spectrum lighting, and of course, specially filtered water and ventilation systems," Jo explains.

Carol becomes horrified at the way she has been living her entire life. Thus begins her brainwashing. . . .

Carol is a victim of her illness and is being promised benefit from the clinic. She is about to start on a program of restrictions which will ultimately bend her will to others. Her ability to reason is being hampered by her extreme level of suffering. She embarks on a rigorous regimen. With this disorientation from her former way of life, a new feeling of security is being established.

Fear of the noises and fear of dying are the factors contributing to this change, along with severe stress and physical exhaustion. If she doesn't conform to this program that she has entered into, she will suffer criticism, ostracism, and resentment from everyone in and connected with the Environmental Health Center.*

"Toni, I have to get out of here, right away!" Carol surveys her hotel room. She is mortified with fear as she grips the phone. "Bobbie—your manager at Rhoden Park—I called her, but I only got her machine. Please, please, you have to help me! I'm getting sicker by the minute! I saw an indoor swimming pool next to the lobby downstairs! I'm breathing in chlorine without even swimming! I'm gasping for breath!" Carol starts to cry and hyperventilate.

*Adapted from a treatise entitled *Thought Reform and Brain Washing* by Hinkle, Wolff, Lifton, and Schein.

"Now hang in there! Bobbie went out. As soon as she returns, I'll talk to her. I think she has one available unit. A fellow is moving out. We'll get back to you just as soon as we know," Toni promises.

"Please hurry!" She looks in the mirror. *I have to try to be strong. There must be something I can do until I get to safe housing and begin the poison treatments.* She's becoming deathly afraid to use the shower. She'll cut her hair shorter. The closer it gets cropped, the more she will rid herself of the poisonous chemicals. She'll be able to wash it in two seconds.

The smells in the beauty shop threaten her life. "Can you please chop my hair off quickly?" The bewildered hair stylist appears flustered. He tries hard to understand his distraught customer, but it's impossible. He simply can't!

"Fred! Help me!" Carol sobs frantically into the phone back in her hotel room. She is hysterical. What is there left to say long distance when she isn't able to validate her torture to him while in the very same room?

"Leave your valuables locked in any available locker in the main office." The sauna employee is personable and helpful. Carol tries to absorb the routine which will become her new way of life. The other women wear large tee shirts and shorts.

"Is my bikini okay?"

"Listen, if I had your figure, I would go naked!" the complimentary sauna lady replies.

Carol doesn't care about compliments. She doesn't care how she looks or acts. She instinctively knows her limitations. She can't tell how or why. She just feels what she can or cannot do. Whatever this demon is and how it makes her act, its restrictions are loud and clear!

She shakes when running the water. The washer and dryer have become too terrifying. Small bikinis are easier to wash. She is not aware of men. She uses skimpy attire like she always wore on far-off beaches. She is here only to get well and recover.

Through the sealed doors, she watches the clock advancing. *Time moves so slowly. It's so hot! I'm so afraid! I hope I don't pass out!* Other patients chat and laugh in the sauna. Carol has lost her ability to enjoy anything. All she can do is cry.

Once out of the heat, she reluctantly swallows the prescribed minerals and nutrients. Her mind now becomes poisoned against anything that isn't considered nonchemical or absolutely pure. She is told to mix two bottles of powder—calcium carbonate and potassium bicarbonate—to form a heartburn remedy. She is supposed to store her bathing suits, which are full of her toxins, in a specified nontoxic bag after each session in the sauna. Everything she learns and does pushes her into a deeper abyss of fear and terror that accompany her uncontrollable and evermounting anxiety.

"What? Your drugs are color dyed? They're blue? That's dangerous! You must use only white pure ones." The intelligent nurse explains the rules. She frowns at Carol's lack of knowledge. "There's a special pharmacy that dispenses drugs without color additives and filters."

She is in a frenzy to correct her mistakes. She can no longer swallow pink, red, yellow, and blue pills. She is frantic to contact the "un-dyeing" medicine store. Everything has to be done at once. She can't waste seconds that could be bringing her help. She needs to stop the torment she is finding harder and harder to bear.

"How soon can you come on out?" Bobbie wants to know.

"As soon as I hang up the phone." Carol can't thank her enough.

Chapter 7

Carol takes a taxi to Rhoden Park. She hugs Bobbie, the manager of the nontoxic housing units.

"Let's make a stack of your 'off-limits,'" Bobbie tells her. She watches Toni and Bobbie sort through her things. All her belongings—toothpaste, dental floss, deodorant, heartburn medicine, colored tissues, and even lipstick—are being ostracized and put into storage. She tries not to touch them. They are contaminated.

She glances at the small trailer in front of her: "Home, Sweet Home." *Will I ever go back to my house? When will I see my family and my little dog again?*

She has been told that her adorable jacket and leather pants are outlawed. She looks over at the storage trailer where she must keep her previously treasured belongings. She shivers in the cool January temperatures in Texas. She wears only a sweater. She needs to detox her allowed clothing quickly before she freezes to death.

"You'll have to wash your clothes at least three times in the products we use. We wear only pure cotton fabrics." Bobbie explains and Carol learns. She thanks the two women who are kind and helpful. Toni leaves, and Bobbie says, "Follow me. I'll show you the kitchen and laundry facilities."

She walks with the manager to a very large mobile unit. She notices about eighteen trailers spread out in a picture-perfect setting. A small lake with swans surrounds the land. How can this "sick camp" have such beautiful scenery? The taxi had taken her from the city to the countryside, past grazing cows, onto a secluded road that leads into a colony of hermits living away from society.

"You get one spoon, one fork, one electric cooker, two plates and pots, a glass, and some sponges. The food and water are ordered and brought in from outside." She tries to assimilate her new lifestyle. As she approaches the rear of the kitchen, she hears the machinery roaring and growling. Bobbie leads the way to the laundry room. Carol lags behind, stricken with anxiety!

She soon finds out that Rhoden Park people are allergic to everything and are afraid to go near her. Several mention that they know she is "out-gassing" from chemicals.

She has felt alone since her illness began. Now she lives all alone in a wilderness.

"After you have washed your clothing several times, people will feel more comfortable near you," she is told. Carol does not think so. She is correct. They still act as if she has the plague. She sadly looks down at her beautiful hand-knit mohair sweater which is on its way to being shrunken. Tears stream down her face. She sits on a small cot. She has a couple of thin cotton blankets for warmth. The tiny trailer houses two small heaters and a chair. The bathroom is as small as the cubicles on cruise ships. The outside wooden porch is shared by a woman named Wilma.

"Carol!" Wilma calls through the connecting wall.

"Yes?"

"Do you have newspaper print in there?"

"No, Wilma." Carol knows she isn't going to have to worry about touching something wrong. Wilma is not going to let her!

Carol doesn't know why she is afraid to leave her assigned seat. Her eyes study the others sitting on similar folding chairs adorning the perimeter of this enormous room. Here at the clinic, in the intradermal skin testing room, people must wait their turn.

A patient is called over to a designated technician. He receives an injection of an allergen in the upper arm. The patient returns to his seat. After the others are injected, the process is repeated using a weaker strain several more times, to bring down the reaction. A red, raised bump warns: "Avoid this particular substance at all costs."

Carol wants to be tested for chemicals. The serums for phenol, formaldehyde, ethanol, newsprint, perfume, cigarette smoke, orris root, and unleaded diesel fuel are on the doctor's prescribed list. Her way of life has changed. She'll do whatever she is told. She wants to live. She does not fear the injections. She fears the room and the people in it.

The technician shocks her. "You're to inject yourself several times a day with the serums I will issue." The nice lady holding the syringe continues, "It's your responsibility to do this." Carol feels herself getting dizzy and sick to her stomach. She prays she'll faint before she throws up.

She is given three different vials of serums: serotonin for headaches and cerebral symptoms; another drug which is a neurotransmitter; and histamine to inject when experiencing a reaction. She is experiencing reactions twenty-four hours a day. The **hisss hisss hisss hisss, tick tick tick ticking** never stops!

"I'll never be able to do this!" Carol tries to stay focused while the nurse inserts the hypodermic needle into her leg.

"Pull back on the plunger. Make sure you don't draw blood. It's really quite easy."

I'm going to die just from watching. If not, most surely when I attempt to do it myself!

"**Y**ou're what? You aren't! Oh, my God!" Fred exclaims in horror. She listens to her husband's words of shock. He tells her that what she's doing is very dangerous!

Carol doesn't know how to tell Fred that she is in worse agony from the testing room than the injections. The immense room terrifies her. It threatens. She constantly glances up at the ceiling, waiting. Soon someone will come to say, "A tidal wave has hit. Evacuate immediately!"

She wants to tell Fred that she needs to die. But she can't. She imagines that death might feel good. She notices damaged cars at the side of the roadway and visualizes the accidents. She hopes for a fatality on her daily 45-minute ride to the clinic and prays to be in it. She wants her life involuntarily removed. She needs to be out of her misery.

Then she feels guilty for her thoughts. She wants to be stronger, to fight, to have a longer life. She wants something to help. She cries long distance, "Fred, no local doctor can help me. You don't know what to do. I have to try anything and everything to overcome this! Do you understand?" She knows his answer before his response: silence. She is so frightened. She is afraid there will never be anyone who will understand.

Carol lies sobbing on her cot in the trailer. She hears howling in the distance.

Are there wolves in this area? How can I be so sick and still miss my little Peanut dog? She longs to hold and hug her dog's small body. Her sobs blend into the howling of the night.

Something's different. Her left ear, which has been making the **click click click, tick tick ticking** noises, now makes a

swish click, swish click, swish click, repeating and repeating. It's so loud she prays for death again to make it stop. She now hears the exact same pattern of **swish click, swish click** in the other ear as well.

She tries not to listen. She places a Walkman a distance from her ears. She hopes to blend some music with the horrible tinnitus. She turns the radio on to seek comfort. Two minutes later, she has to turn it off. She puts the earplugs in. Two minutes later, she takes the earplugs out. There is no comfort zone. The **swish click, swish click, swish click, swish click** penetrates above every sound in the universe.

Carol reaches again for the earplugs. Everything is worse! She dials the emergency number for the clinic. *Surely they'll send out an ambulance to save my life.* An automated machine asks her to leave a message. She cries into the machine. She begs the machine to send an ambulance to Rhoden Park.

She runs to the kitchen looking for consolation. The place is deserted. Everyone is asleep. Her only companion is a good-sized rat. Mr. Rat is searching for food. Carol already has seen dozens of ants. Her food is organic. Nothing has been sprayed. What's one large rat and some ants compared to what she has?

Carol notices a lower volume of tinnitus while she is in the sweltering sauna. This reinforces her treatment plan. She forces herself to increase therapy workouts until she is exhausted. She sits on the scalding benches inside the sauna. She drinks water and prays for relief. Carol sees the same fellow each day taking treatments. His name is Dave, just like her son. Dave comes from Virginia. He seems kind and understanding. They are becoming friends.

Dave tells her he suffers from a reaction to chemicals used in his painting business. He has a car and frequently takes her to the approved store where the environment is safe. They buy organic products and eat organic lunch.

Carol tries to control her anxiety and sobbing, especially around Dave. She tries to conceal the terror she feels in her surroundings, but Dave sees the fear in her eyes. How can she explain what she doesn't understand herself? She needs a friend. She can't be by herself. She will not survive this program alone. Others faint and get sick from the sauna. Carol pushes on.

Rhoden Park people have a driver, "Murray and his van." Murray's father owns the property and the trailer park where Carol now lives. Murray arrives at the campsite at 7:45 a.m. to pick up patients for the clinic. He is required to change his clothing before he enters the compound. He returns to the AEHC no later than 6:00 p.m. to drive everyone back.

Murray is a kind man. He hopes Carol will soon be well. Murray carries gallons of filtered water into her trailer. She uses only clean water for everything. She washes her dishes in filtered water. She is terrified of doing anything outside the code of ethics she has been indoctrinated into. If she does, she is convinced, she will immediately become worse.

Carol waits at the clinic for Murray. She sits on the cement floor in the hallway. She is curled into a ball. She finishes her treatments by noon. She phones Murray and cries, asking him to hurry. She goes back on the floor in her designated safe place. She feels like climbing the walls. She does not know that she suffers from tranquilizer withdrawal symptoms.

She cannot wait each day to go back to the camp, only to have to wash her clothes, prepare and eat her food, inject herself, drug herself, and try to sleep in order to wake up and start all over again.

She sneaks into a warm waiting room with furniture. She needs to get off the cold floor. "You cannot wait in this room," the registered nurse from the clinic, who spies, announces. "You must adhere to the rules. You must wait only where the environment is sterile." Patients have trouble holding up to this strict regimen. She wills her strength to endure.

Carol stands by her trailer door. It's impossible to lock such an unaligned door. She looks into the star-filled night for a light on in someone else's trailer. She looks for any signs of life in the noisy night. She tries to reassure herself as to her safety. She thinks of burglars coming into the camp to loot and maim the sick occupants who would be easy marks. She has been told, "Don't worry, Carol. Bobbie's husband has a gun!"

She awakens after only two hours of sleep. The tinnitus seems to be gone! Then she hears **boom boom boom boom.** *Oh, my God!* There is nothing she can do. She has to weather whatever is happening, but just what is it? She doesn't have a soul to visit at this hour, except Mr. Rat in the kitchen.

A television is suspended from the ceiling opposite her bed. It has a remote control. The winter Olympics are on. She would love to watch. She misses everything she has lost. The television is another foe. She is afraid to turn it on for fear of how it will act toward her.

A woman who speaks Spanish offers to clean her trailer for a token fee. She wants to pray for Carol. She chants, "Madre de Dios, por favor ayuda esta pobre mujer." ("Mother of God, please help this poor woman.")

Afflicted is what Carol is. Poor is what she and her husband are rapidly becoming!

Carol looks at the blood and piece of tooth in the bath-room sink. The chemical-free dental floss is a hazard. The thought of what another tooth mishap entails now fills her with utter terror and dread. Every previous small problem has blos-somed into gigantic proportions. She sobs hysterically. Her toothpaste is off limits. Her dental floss is banned. She brushes with baking soda. She adheres to the program conscientiously.

Now the bleeding won't stop. She has destroyed one whole tooth using the coarse, crummy dental floss. She can't bear any more. Her anxiety and stress from the tinnitus are as bad as the horrible noises. She compounds her emotional problems with her cumbersome way of living. She is so afraid to use anything that hasn't been approved—anything that will worsen her condition.

"We'll take you to the dentist," a young man says.

Carol looks at Chris and his girlfriend who live in Rhoden Park. They are not old enough to live with such limitations. Yet they function in a way that is not humanly possible for her.

Later, she waits outside the dentist's office looking for Chris's car. She hadn't cared that this dentist who uses accepted environmental health procedures had seen her crying. She is out of control from the torture that limits her ability to function.

"Taxi!" She runs back into the dental office screaming and crying. "Please help me, someone. I'm dying! Can you call a taxi for me?"

"Our dentist does good work," the receptionist says seriously. "No one has ever died before." The office worker looks puzzled. She thinks Carol is in dire straits from their dental work.

Carol watches the newly arrived married couple wash their clothes and bedding over and over and over. They use the same machines that she runs from. The husband and wife were poisoned from a mattress. They have constant burning throughout their bodies. They move from place to place seeking help. They have been on television, too.

Other people are suffering. She knows that. But they can smile, talk, and laugh. Carol can only cry. She is still frantic.

Chapter 8

"Is this safe?"

"Yes. Everything we give our patients is safe," a nurse replies.

No one seems to want to hurt anyone further. Carol consoles herself with this thought. Only in her case, it would be impossible for her to be hurting anymore than she already is.

She shakes with fright. A technician inserts a needle into her vein for an intravenous procedure. She is terrified but has agreed to take this treatment that her doctor has ordered.

"Why isn't an MD or nurse doing this?"

"Because there is nothing to the procedure. It's very simple." The not-too-sociable technician leaves. The needle and solution burn her arm. She tries not to look at the blood that has squirted out. She feels sick to her stomach.

"Now don't be a baby." She looks up at one of the other patients who is taking an intravenous. "I love these treatments. I feel so much better afterwards. Don't you?"

"I hate it!" Carol worries that the solution of saline and magnesium can injure her healthy body. The liquid sears through her arm like a raging fire. She nervously glances at the bottle to see how much longer she has to go. She is determined to finish the whole treatment. She vows not to complain or call for help, as she winces in pain.

"Does the bottle have to be completely empty before you are done?" she asks the intravenous lover.

"You're paying for it, honey. You might as well enjoy it."

Carol looks down, alarmed! Blood has been dripping from the connection in her vein for the past hour and a half. Her jeans are drenched in red liquid.

"Help!"

"My gosh, you poor darling! You've been sitting, suffering like this for hours?" A new technician has come to her aid.

"Yes. I didn't want to complain."

"Well, you should have! Do you want the rest of your IV? I can reconnect it in the other arm and you can finish it off."

Carol sadly nods "yes." Tears stream down her face. She hopes the IV treatment is the *only* thing that will be finished off.

No one can say I wasn't brave! Carol enters the trailer.

All of a sudden, the ground is spinning and shifting. She is nauseated. She is going to throw up.

"No, this can't be! I can't stand any more!"

The sounds of swishing and clicking have sped up. What is even stranger is that the **swish-click** noise in one ear echoes the same variation in the other, except the **click** is resounding in one ear when the other is on a **swish**. One ear is **swish, click, swish, clicking** while the other is **click, swish, click, swishing**. This doesn't make sense!

She struggles not to throw up from the IV and the noises. She struggles to live through the night. She wants to give up on Texas. She's not ready to give up on her life, though. She is only ready to throw up!

Carol calls home to everyone. "I'm not lasting in Texas. I'm falling apart."

Fred promises to fly out after April 15. He promises to stay with her for more treatment time. Carol has already spent a large part of his hard-earned money. Fred is always so generous. "Go rent a car. Pay for housing close to the clinic. Buy whatever you need."

"I can't!" she cries.

All the things that she has done so easily before are now totally impossible. She has her hands full just living through each day. The rigorous heat therapy she is subjecting her body and mind to is exhausting.

Toni invites the poison victim to walk behind the encampment in a deserted, wooded area. Carol reluctantly accepts the invitation. Walking is healthy. Toni is nice. Toni educates her. "Back in the olden days, people detoxed their bodies through exercise."

Carol ponders this. *How much exercise can a human body do? I biked from city to city, snow skied all winter, and swam the entire summer. How on earth have these toxins attacked me with all this exercise?*

The head physician studies Carol's blood chemistry panels.

"I'm not getting any better. In fact, I'm worse. How can this be? I'm injecting myself with serums. I take multiple forty-five-minute saunas one after another. I even took your intravenous and got sick from it!"

"Go back into the sauna! You need more treatment time! You have gasoline solvents in your blood!"

Gasoline? His harshness shocks her into facing facts. She has challenged him. She quickly makes an appointment with each of this doctor's colleagues.

The other medical doctor looks up from Carol's blood panels. "Something is weird here."

Is that it? After months of treatment and all this money, I have "weird"? She leaves his office feeling the same way she came in—miserable.

Carol doesn't think her appointment can be much worse with the other doctor. She finds out differently. He is an osteopath.

"Just lie back and relax. This might make a big difference. In fact, it could take away your whole problem."

"Go ahead then."

Carol has never had an adjustment before. She hates anything being done to her body. She hates pills. Now she hates doctors. But she can't afford to bypass anything. She hears the snap of her neck and thinks *this* was something to bypass.

Later in the trailer she becomes more panic stricken. She suffers through a horrible aurora migraine. She is positive her adjustment was the culprit.

Isn't she doing everything she's been told to do? The answer is yes. So she stays, compounding her torture with more torture. She tries repeatedly to get an ambulance, but to no avail. She buys an oxygen tank with all the paraphernalia, but her fellow recluses won't let her use it—the tubing is wrong. Plastic is banned and forbidden.

The floor in the hallway of the clinic is too cold. She waits hours for a ride back to the compound after her sauna treatments each day. Then she washes her bathing suits three times. She must eliminate the poisons in them before she can prepare dinner in the freezing kitchen.

Her airline ticket is no longer valid. It has expired, just like she will soon. Carol has to purchase a new ticket. Fred has already prepaid for a round-trip ticket so that he can visit her. Gallons of filtered water with a full (and expensive) week's load of groceries have just been delivered. Regardless, it is time to leave. She must do it quickly and quietly.

If anyone sees me, they will try to stop me. Aren't verbal confrontations just as harmful as physical abuse? Haven't the experts proven that?

She decides to leave at daybreak, when everyone is still sleeping.

In the kitchen at dinnertime, Carol hands Chris her chemistry panel readings. "See what you think. I rely on your opinion with your law degree and mercury poisoning experience."

"God, I wish my panels read like this," he says.

She is surprised. "What about my gasoline reading?"

"It's not really above normal."

Chris's words repeat in her thoughts along with the **swish, click, swish, click, click, swish, click, swish** that is still as loud as a jet. She starts to figure out what won't fit into her suitcase.

Fred hears her frantic sobs and words over the phone from the trailer park. She is adamant about leaving. He doesn't try to change her mind. He will be waiting at the airport to welcome her back into their home—she hopes!

Carol is returning worse than when she left. She looks at the packing work ahead. Fred has shipped additional clothing per her many requests, but for the wrong climate. She has been trudging through snow in February. She looks sadly at Fred's hopeful words of encouragement and love on his Valentine's Day card. She removes the card from the trailer wall.

"Come home well. With all my love," she rereads. Tears block her vision as she squeezes her clothes into the suitcase. She looks down at the leather pants and jacket she has retrieved from the storage unit. She thinks of Sylvia, her other childhood friend. Sylvia is attractive with impeccable taste.

Carol vacillates. *What do I need these beautiful clothes for? I'm heading toward death. But Sylvia will never let me live it down if I leave my jacket. Fred won't even notice. I don't have room anyway. Do I really care about anything now? My life is only pain and suffering. What's going to happen to me?*

"Are you crazy?" Bobbie says. Carol has been caught!

Toni is running toward her, screaming. The taxicab driver loads her suitcase.

"You'll never make it home on the airline with those ears of yours! Your husband won't be able to help you. He'll throw you into a mental ward." Carol hears Toni's words as the curse she thinks they could be.

"Send me my things, please!" She sobs furiously. She reaches out the open window of the cab and grabs the outstretched hands of the two women she has grown so very fond of. Their touch releases as the driver slowly moves the taxi forward.

Carol looks back through the cab's rear window. The gravel dust from the cab pulling out flies into the women's faces. Their expressions of utter shock leave a deep foreboding within her, as do the words she prays will never come true.

Somehow, she makes it home on the plane.

Chapter 9

Carol is happy to see Fred. However, she fears the feeling will not last long. She has always felt protected near him, but whatever is causing her pain dominates the security he gives. His hug and kiss feel good. *Why do I have this feeling that I am supposed to be thankful that Fred is allowing me back into my own home?*

"I hope now your behavior will be different."

Her feelings are correct. How is she to answer? Nothing has changed. She had been afraid of the airport here. The **hissing,** like her pressure cooker, along with the **clicking,** is driving her insane. Not only is she tortured, but now she also has a different lifestyle to adhere to. She has to make Fred understand that everything around the house will have to be changed to accommodate her new needs.

"You're scaring her," Fred says. Carol feels herself growing furious after being home for only two minutes. Peanut is *her* dog. She picked her out as a puppy. She has cared for her since she was eight weeks old. Carol swears that she will die before she ever leaves her again.

She is crushed as Peanut darts away from her outstretched hands. "Stop! Peanut! Stop right now!" Peanut does, too. On a dime! This adorable black yorkie's vocabulary includes exactly what stop means!

Carol scoops her little animal into her arms. Peanut licks the tears sliding down her owner's sad face. She wiggles with excitement. Carol holds her tight, returning her licks with kisses. She is overwhelmed with the love she feels for her darling pet.

"Where's her food dish, Fred?"

"I removed everything. I'll go get it."

"What did you use in here? It smells funny."

"I saw some ants on the patio. I sprayed with Raid."

"No! Oh, no! Are you trying to kill me?"

"Take it easy. I won't do it again. I didn't realize it could hurt you."

"I can't be around any chemicals. They caused my problem. I can't help it!" She is racked with sobs again. "I don't mean to cause you trouble!" She regrets being demanding, but her fears control past logic.

"All of this stuff has to go out of the house at once!" Carol cries. She yanks down the laundry detergent along with her wool cleaner, dishwashing detergent, fabric softener, bleach, all-purpose cleaner, shoe polish—the list of products she has to remove seems endless. She finishes in the laundry and kitchen area and moves onto the bathrooms. She can't rid the house of toxins fast enough. Fred looks on in amazement. The shelves are becoming bare right before his eyes.

"You can't wear aftershave anymore. Please, just use products that won't hurt me." She cries about the inconvenient regimen she must follow if she is to survive.

Fred is in a state of shock. Carol thinks he will honor her requests, though. After all, hasn't she just spent some $20,000 at a poison center?

"I need a sauna installed in the house and a water filtering system. I can't touch any of this food in the refrigerator. It all has to be organic." Carol hits Fred with a lot at one time. His mouth hangs open. He stares at her, disbelievingly.

"I'll drive you to get organic groceries, if that's what you need," Fred says, looking defeated.

"Bless you." Carol is relieved. She gives him a kiss. Fred will lose a whole day in his office, traveling to stores that sell organic food. *He wants to keep me alive!* She appreciates his cooperation. Fred has a load to digest. She still has some wits about her, but the evil force that threatens is bent on removing them. It has taken control of her. Carol's mind is as strongly conditioned from the poison center as from the fear and terror that consume her every movement.

Haven't I done well? One day home from Texas, and I already have a doctor lined up. He is not only an orthomolecular MD, but a nutritionist, an immunologist, and even a psychiatrist as well. The psychiatry degree ought to please Fred.

Nothing she does seems to faze her husband. His demeanor stays the same, just like her **click hisss, click hisss** in one ear and **hisss click, hisss click** in the other.

Carol observes her new doctor in San Francisco. He documents her extensive medical saga as she talks on and on. She knows he is expensive, but well worth it! He glances at his time clock every now and then. Fred will have to pay him $300 per hour and $100 for telephone conversations. She feels sick over the money that saving her life is costing. She tries not to dwell on that fact. Where could she find another doctor as well educated as this one? Surely he'll solve her mystery.

"I'm going to run off blood work. I think you have an irritated acoustic nerve which will probably heal in about three months."

"Hooray!" Finally, she has a different diagnosis. Something inside her head is irritated. His words are sweet music to her ears, unlike the horrific music of tinnitus.

"Go into the outer office. Jane will start you on antioxidant tablets with vitamins and minerals."

In three months, I won't be hearing all these sounds. Great! I sure picked out the right doctor, thanks to my friend Dave Zodun in Texas. Lucky for me, Dave had a list of environmental doctors with him. What would I have done without this list?

"Do you want a vitamin B shot?" Jane asks.

"I didn't realize you were a nurse."

"I'm not, but I give shots all the time."

Carol is reluctant. "If this will make me better, go ahead." The shot is painful. She can't sit down. "I've never heard of any of these pills." She glances over at Jane's computer which is totaling hundreds of dollars for vitamins and minerals. And this is only her first visit! She reads: B complex; vitamin E, 400 iu; buffered C, 1/2 tsp.; carnitine, 2 250-mg capsules; CoQ, 30 mg. *What is this stuff?* She rips open the packaging and gulps down everything right in the office. She can't wait to get better.

That evening, she hears a loud blast of noise. It peters out and is gone. She phones her new doctor.

"Just swallow an extra dose of what I gave you. That should counteract the sound." She does. *It* doesn't!

"**Y**our cholesterol level is low." Her new doctor looks disturbed. "People who have low cholesterol seem prone to these types of conditions." *Doesn't everyone in the world want low cholesterol?* "I want you to eat a high fat diet. You should use real butter and eat meat with lots of animal fat like lamb."

Guess not!

"Here is a food list which will guide you."

He's the doctor. I love fat!

Your tests all came out negative."

Is it any wonder?

Each minute passes like a day as Carol tries to endure her suffering. She barely gets a couple of hours of sleep at night.

She takes heavy doses of tranquilizers just to exist with her tinnitus. Meanwhile, her doctor keeps adding on every possible health supplement and technique known to humans. The bottles of capsules, powders, and liquids need a whole storage cabinet of their own. Fred buys one, too!

The doctor's three months to heal will soon be over. Everything, though, is much worse. "You have a cast iron stomach," Fred used to say, watching Carol eat. Now he says, "Don't skip any of your pills," as he watches her swallow capsules the size of gum balls. Oddly, her stomach is still holding up, while her emotions are falling apart.

Yours would, too, if you took all of this as directed!

START:
Pyridoxine (B6), 250 mg
Thiamine (B1), 2 100-mg tablets
Allithiamine 1 50-mg capsule

TWICE A DAY WITH MEALS:
Multi VM (no copper or iron), 2 capsules
B complex, 1 capsule
Vitamin E, 400 iu
Buffered C, l/2 tsp.
Carnitine, 2 250-mg capsules
Co Q, 30 mg
NA-Cysteine, 2 500-mg capsules
Selenium, 200 mcg
Ginkgo, 1 capsule
Lecithin, 2 capsules
Folinic acid, 0.8 mg
Flax (ground powder), 1 tsp.
Cod liver oil, 1 tsp. per day
Thioctic, 100 mg
Sphingolin, 1 tablet
Arginine, 4 500-mg capsules
Copper sebacate, 4 mg
Octacosanol, 5,000 mcg
Cavinton, 5 mg twice a day (dissolve under tongue)

DMSO, 10 drops (1/2 ml) applied to small cotton plug in right ear twice a day. Be sure ear is clean. (Carol is instructed to use DMSO in the other ear as well.)

Magnets, green side in front of ear lobe under Velcro headband twice a day for two- to eight-hour periods.

Melatonin, 3 mg (two at bedtime)

Olbas inhaler, 1 sniff twice per day

Ponaris nose drops, 1 drop in each nostril at bedtime

"You're going to be the healthiest person on the block," Bethann encourages her friend by phone. Carol doesn't have to worry how to fill her time or her stomach. It's only Fred's wallet that is empty.

"I'm afraid to drive my car! How will I get more treatments if I can't get there?" she cries out to her family.

"I'll help you drive, Mom," David says. Her son interrupts his life to aid his sick mother. He drives her to the doctor. His love and devotion are quite obvious. It pains her to see the sadness in his eyes when he looks at what she has become. She prays to be strong. David motivates her to endure. He begs her to keep fighting. He becomes a focal point for her survival.

Carol is still terrified on the freeways, even with David driving. She can't figure out why. The cars appear different as they zoom by. When the ignition is turned off, her tinnitus seems suddenly quieter. Part of what is terrifying her is instantly diminished, but it doesn't make sense.

Her refrigerator still scares her. It has been her old friend. Too bad it has to go. It's only a matter of time.

Carol concludes that her tinnitus makes everything sound off-kilter and terrifying. She lies in bed listening to sounds. Cars pulling into neighboring driveways clang. Their tone goes up and down on a melodic scale, repeating and repeating. *I'm going to go nuts!* The refrigerator resounds through the walls. It hums its same loud, ominous chant. The noise jumps back and forth with changing frequency pitches that play havoc with her. *Why aren't any of the noises running straight like they used to? The hideous outer sounds beat in rhythms of my tinnitus.*

"Oh, my God!" She screams out in horror. *Every straight tone that I come in contact with duplicates my pulsating tinnitus!*

Carol's conscientious doctor keeps trying new treatments. She hysterically pleads with him to make her well. She's finding it impossible to live.

The doctor tells Fred, "Keep a watch on her. She might be suicidal!"

Chapter 10

The vitamins and minerals haven't repaired the damaged nerve as the doctor thought they would, so he starts prescribing other things.

Carol pours DMSO down her ears per the MD's instructions. She is told that DMSO is a horse liniment that has a healing effect on humans. The doctor gives her a magnetic headband to wear over her ears for healing. He prescribes nose drops. She takes everything he suggests in heavy doses. She still pleads for more. "Help me! Please help me!"

She tells him, "I need to end my life if you can't make me better. My life is slipping away. I don't know how to stop it. I don't know how to end it."

"Fred! Look what happened." Fred stares at the Drexel night-stand of their cherished bedroom set.

"I knocked over the DMSO bottle. I was mixing it, like the doctor told me, with the iodine solution to put in my ears and nose. I got it all over my clothes." She sobs uncontrollably.

"Don't worry about the furniture." Carol is instantly thankful for a good quality in her husband's makeup. Fred never seems bothered by serious mishaps.

How much more suffering and pain can I endure? Nothing is better. Everything is worse.

Carol adds the doctor's designated amount of straight iodine into the filtered tap water and drinks it according to his instructions.

"This is the antibiotic used long ago, before modern medicine," her doctor tells her.

What Carol says is very different, as she looks in the mirror. "I'm a total mess! My entire face and body have broken out in white pimples." Her eyes drip from constant tears and conjunctivitis. She shakes with fear and terror round the clock and from the clock, too, with its constant **tick tick tick tick**. . . .

She distinguishes more tinnitus sounds. Her condition is progressing. Why? Nothing makes sense to her and, obviously, even less to Fred or her doctor. She hears church bells—**clang, clang, clang**—a very high-pitched flute-like sound—**e-e-e-e-e-e**—high-frequency beating tones—**ding dong, ding dong, ding dong, ding dong**—lower-frequency harp tones resounding back and forth—**bing bong, bing bong, bing bong, bing bong**—with the constant **hisss hisss hisss swish swish swishing** noises mixed in. How is she supposed to tolerate this? How is she supposed to live with this? The worst part is that all of these sounds are going on at the same time!

"Take it out of here! I can't stand it another minute." Carol looks at the refrigerator that she has used in such good health. She cries nonstop.

"It's about time we bought a new one anyway," Fred sighs.

"Can you go by yourself to pick out another one? Please just make sure it's quiet," she whimpers.

Fred says, "I'm not buying another one, unless you come with me to pick it out." She does.

Carol shudders. She visualizes the refrigerators sitting in a row waiting to attack. That's because they are. The appliance customers find Carol much more intriguing than the refrigerators. She is jumping out of her skin and can't stop running around the store.

At home, her mouth waters, as she looks at forbidden food housed in her new refrigerator. She is still terrified of eating anything that isn't organic. In addition, an orchestra of tinnitus music plays with no mercy.

"Do you have an organic salad?" The waiter has never heard anyone ask that before. Carol is drooling. The waiter prepares salads for everyone at the dinner table except her.

Fred has encouraged Carol to see their good friends, Sylvia and Ron. "It'll do you good to get out like we used to."

Outside? No! No! Not outside!

"You look great! No one can see your earplugs. No one but you knows there's anything wrong," Sylvia reassures her friend from teen years. Carol tries to act calm and normal, but it is difficult. She has to walk by a band that serenades the happy dinner guests. Her only goal is to reach the bathroom.

In the car driving home, Carol's sobs turn to anguish. She had denied herself all the food on the menu. In addition, she playacted a performance of being fine that deserves an Academy Award. Everything in the restaurant had scared her. She has held in her emotions until now. She frantically cries out for sympathy from Fred. "I'm so miserable! I can't go on anymore! A flute is playing. Church bells are clanging. A high-pitched trumpet is blaring. Steam is hissing. I can't last. Dear God, why can't you help me?"

Fred immediately starts making up a song: "She hears a flute, she hears a train, she hears bells, and she hears trumpets. She can't eat and she can't sleep." He laughs at his creativity at having composed his own little lyrics.

Fred thinks he's funny! His wife wants to die, but before I do, I want him to have my condition. Then if I don't kill him first, it will!

When they get home, Carol screams at him for his lack of feelings. Fred gathers up a few items. "I'm leaving! I'm not going to stay another minute with you!"

Carol hates him, yet she wonders why she wants him to stay. "You can't leave me alone," she hysterically rants. "I'll kill myself!" He disregards her threats.

"I need to get away from you! You're a lunatic!" He runs out the back of the house. The door closes hard. It resounds like the earthquake that has crushed out her life.

She cries and cries. *Why do I even want him around with his humiliating antics, mimicking my torture? He acts like an unfeeling creature! I don't understand this constant terror. I don't know why I can't do things anymore. I don't know why I test appliances to find the quietest models. I don't know why the whole world is off-limits to me!* Her actions come across irrational not only to others, but also to herself. Something has possessed her!

Carol wants someone with her constantly. She needs comfort and consolation. Fred agrees to come back if she promises to act better.

Once again, Helen has returned. Carol must not be alone. Now she has both Peanut and Helen to take care of. Peanut to walk and Helen to cook for. Helen's aged while Carol's been busy dying. She can't figure out which one is more work—Helen, who is now incontinent and makes messes, or her adored animal child—who always did make messes.

Carol pleads for more help. The doctor issues more. Now she is instructed to mix lidocaine with the DMSO. She pours solutions down her nose and into her ears. She gags from the horrible tastes. She is relentless in her obedience to her doctor's orders. He gives her a magnetic board to sleep on. Carol doesn't question anything. She follows every instruction precisely. She swallows massive quantities of tablets and capsules. She alternates between praying for relief and praying for death. She can't act differently, even though Fred is back. He had stayed away for a couple of days. He looks happy after his reprieve. He looks rejuvenated and ready for—what?—her impending death?

Helen now seems as unworried about Carol as Fred appears to be. Only Peanut looks and acts bewildered.

Fred completely ignores his wife's pleas for emotional support. On the other hand, he goes far out of his way to physically help her. He does all the grocery shopping. He even drives long distances to special health food stores. Carol's feelings for Fred fluctuate, just like his actions do. She knows that if her finger were to bleed, he would immediately put a bandage on the wound and kiss it. *Why can't he just kiss me and say he's sorry I'm suffering?* She needs him now more than she has throughout their entire marriage.

"**A**re you hyperacusic?" her doctor asks.

"What's that?" Carol questions.

"Never mind. If you were hyperacusic, you wouldn't be able to hear my voice."

"Oh? I can translate verbatim the painters' conversation from your neighbor's house. They're speaking Spanish."

"Good! Come in here." He pats his examination table. "Just sit here for a minute and give me your arm."

"What're you going to do?"

"I want to test your pain threshold." The doctor inserts a needle.

"What was in that?"

"Nothing! Just an empty syringe with a long needle. You certainly have a high pain tolerance."

He doesn't believe me either.

No amount of physical torture to her body can come close to what she is experiencing. She is expected to let everyone around her alone. Only she can't.

"Carol, I have bad news for you," her sister-in-law says.

She holds the phone. Her body quivers. She starts to sob uncontrollably. She knows what Dixie has called to say. She needs to stop the words. It has been only a couple of weeks since Dixie last called. She remembers their conversation so clearly.

"Your brother is in the hospital." She hears Dixie through her cries of anguish. She cries for her brother, Charlie, and she cries for herself. "It looks bad."

Then a few days later . . . "Carol, come quickly! Your brother is on the phone from the hospital," Fred tells her. "He called on the fax phone."

Carol leaves her bed. She stops frozen in the living room. She can't move. She has to walk past the refrigerator. Then she has to stand under the fluorescent lights to talk on this particular phone. She can't do it. She can't do it for good news, let alone for the voice with the pain that belongs to her brother.

"Are you coming, Carol?" Fred coaxes and pushes the phone toward her. The cord expands as far as it will reach. Charlie is in critical condition. "His voice is fading, Carol. Do you want me to talk for you?" her husband wants to know.

"Yes." *I have no choice, Charlie. This thing won't let me. Please forgive me! Dear God!* Whatever it is, it refuses to let her reach the phone. It won't allow her to use the area where that phone is installed. It is allowing her less and less with each passing day.

"You chose the wrong one, God!" she angrily screams out. "Why can't I die instead!" Her wails of sorrow continue until she collapses.

Now today, Carol hears, "Your brother is dead!" Dixie's words have finished off what is left of her heart.

"No! No! Not him! Let me die! I need to die! Why can't I be the one that is dead! I don't understand. Where are you, God?" Her screams of anguish do not sound human. Over and over she recalls: *I was too afraid to walk underneath the fluorescent lights, past the refrigerator, and to the phone. I failed my brother!* She had one chance to say good-bye to her only sibling. Now he is gone forever. Carol lives waiting for the end of her own life. She waits and waits . . . so alone.

Chapter 11

"That stuff is as harmless as popcorn," the orthomolecular doctor says on the phone. He tries unsuccessfully to reassure her. Carol worries about the drugs she's forced to take. Her mother's past mute condition from a stroke is always close by. It reminds her of what can happen to the brain.

How would this doctor like to swallow 30 milligrams of Serax with two full milligrams of Klonopan plus melatonin and sleeping pills—to stay alive? Of course no one believes that I'm trying to go on living. They probably think I have a permanent mental condition. I wonder if my friends think this is a phase, like menopause. They sure have deserted me. It shows how much faith anyone has in me. None!

She berates herself for needing drugs. "Which do I prefer, pills or death?" she keeps asking herself. She knows that her brother would have wanted her to continue the pills and to fight. She studies and researches causes and more suggested treatments for tinnitus. Why isn't anything working?

"**A**cupuncture? In San Francisco Chinatown?" Carol is trying everything else. *Should I?* "How will I get there?"

"I'll take you," Mitch, her childhood friend, offers.

If he thinks this is a positive treatment, then maybe?

"I'm afraid of the parking garage," she confesses.

"I'll pick you up in front of your doctor's office."

She is desperate to know why she can force herself to function for short spans in some places better than others. It's as if this "thing" picks the places to get her!

Mitch and Carol talk on their way to Chinatown. They had met when she was very young. Only Bethann knew how much she liked him. Now years later, only Bethann and Mitch acknowledge that there is something dreadful that causes her pain and odd behavior.

"I keep asking myself why, why is this happening, Carol?" her dearest friend Bethann says, long distance.

"How can I not believe you, Carol? I've never heard you complain about a medical condition in your whole life," Mitch says locally.

"I bet you'd like to go live with Mitch," Fred says, right in their own home. Carol doesn't think she stands a chance of living at all, regardless of with whom or where she lives.

She shakes from fright as she lies on the acupuncture table. She has never done this before. The needles stick out of her head and earlobes. They are connected to batteries that vibrate. She hears the vibrations differently from the Chinese doctor looking down at her. She tells him that her life is a living nightmare!

She can no longer control her outbursts. She is dizzy and collapses on the floor crying. She holds onto the walls. She is afraid to move, to shower, to brush her teeth. She is heading toward death. Soon she will join her brother and parents. Still, no one believes her. Her husband makes fun of her.

"Mom, Dad, Charlie, I need you!"

She kneels in prayer. *Do I have the ability to save myself anymore? Do I have the ability to commit suicide? Have I left any stone unturned?*

71

"Ten thousand dollars?" Fred exclaims.

Does amalgamate cause tinnitus? Could this save her?

Carol is still brainwashed, clinging to her environmental health rules and regulations. Now she's at a dental specialist who believes that metal fillings can cause all kinds of problems, including tinnitus.

She tells the amalgamate dentist and hygienist, "No one else can possibly have tinnitus like I do."

The dental hygienist replies, "I know someone." Carol gets the name and makes a phone call.

Norina Trucco sounds nice. She has a life despite suffering from tinnitus. She has seen Carol's orthomolecular doctor in San Francisco. She has tried several of the same treatments Carol has undergone. Norina knows what tinnitus is. She just doesn't know what to do about it. *Why isn't she afraid of it like I am? Why?*

Carol needs to determine if anything has been overlooked. She returns to two ENT specialists. One is polite as he bids her farewell. The other doesn't deserve a medical license. "Here are four pages of psychiatrists. Do yourself a favor and see one."

He is very rude. He pushes his office window open after she repeatedly closes it. Carol attempts to reduce her fear. It seems to be entering through his open window. Sometimes it's inside, and sometimes it's outside. Which is it?

"Are you absolutely sure that this isn't dangerous?" Her orthomolecular doctor hears her crying to live and crying to die. "You want me to swallow four of these huge 500-mg tablets of niacin wax matrix three times a day? That's 6,000 mg per day of niacin?" *If I overdose, I need to make sure I finish off the job. I don't want to end up like my mother.*

"Yes, that's correct," Carol hears him say. She is sure she has his designated dosage correct.

David's and Fred's birthdays are two days apart. Carol has struggled to stay in the car. Now she struggles to stay in Julius Castle, a beautiful restaurant in San Francisco. *I'm supposed to be celebrating—my death,* she morbidly thinks.

Fred's favorite place to eat has the most breathtaking view of the entire Bay Area. It is a truly special place to dine. Her family consumes delicious dinners. Carol can only eat a portion of hers. She needs the food to mix with the magnitude of drugs she is taking.

She swallows the next dose of 2,000 mg of niacin. Fred drinks wine and talks to David. Carol is going to die soon. She sits looking at the family she loves that will soon be lost to her. She tries to get through the last birthday celebration she expects to see.

"Please go get Helen and bring her back to the house again, Fred," Carol had begged her husband before their birthday celebration. Helen has been shuttled back and forth between their two homes like a ping-pong ball bouncing back and forth over the net. Now it's crucial to have Helen stay with her at all times.

Carol looks over at Helen snoring on the far side of Carol's king-size bed. Fred has moved into the guest bedroom. Something is wrong. Carol's nausea becomes overwhelming. She races toward the bathroom, but it's far too late! She retches her insides out, watching the niacin tablets spew all over the bedroom carpet along with her bile.

Fred acts quickly. The paramedics strap Carol to the stretcher. Helen is still snoring.

Carol hears the emergency room doctor's voice. "She has a dangerously high liver reading. Your wife has hepatitis from the overdose of niacin!"

Why haven't I died? She can no longer tolerate her suffering.

"I'm so afraid!" she says to the staff physician and Fred. She means afraid of the hospital structure. Her mysterious condition still takes precedence over the liver damage she has just incurred from her orthomolecular doctor's treatment. Now she has no more faith in her doctor, but she doesn't have anyone else to turn to. She is even worse with all the emergency staff around. The very thing that is taking her life has shown itself again in the hospital. Why is it more apparent in some places than in others? What is it, and how does it appear? Will she ever know before she dies?

She listens to the swooshing sounds that are as loud as the train system. She hears the church bells, the squeals, the clicking and beating noises, and knows . . . she has absolutely no quality of life left. None!

OCTOBER, 1994

Carol is barely hanging on. No one else knows this.

"Oh, my God! Help me! Fred!"

She stands frozen in horror, sobbing uncontrollably, as usual. She stares at her stove in disbelief. "Look at the pot! I don't know why I ran out of the kitchen after I put water up to boil. Look what happened. I've ruined everything. The pot and stove are scaring me!" She covers her ears, sobbing her heart out.

The crackling of the melting aluminum merges with the burner. The sound resembles chunks of cement being broken away by the drill of a construction worker. Only she hears it. Only she experiences the pain and fear. And only Carol still thinks there is a rational problem to diagnose.

She feels Fred's arm around her, but his words are less than consoling. "I want you to agree to sign yourself into the psychiatric ward immediately. It's the right thing to do. You have to learn coping techniques."

She notices his voice and mannerisms. *He's treating me like I'm demented.*

"I'll call the doctor right away! If you don't cooperate, I'm going to move out!"

Carol nods her head in compliance. Tears stream down her face. She is a beaten, injured woman. No one will ever understand how she feels. How can they? She doesn't understand it herself!

Chapter 12

"Is someone on duty all night?" Carol notices that the voluntary mental unit looks shiny and new. She is glad her room is directly opposite the nurses' station. She wants people near her. She is deathly afraid of being alone.

"You didn't bring in any pills with you, did you?" the nurse on duty asks. Carol watches her suitcase being searched.

"No." She looks over at Fred. He knows that she has pills. *They're in my jacket pocket.* She knows Fred understands that she will die without her drugs. He doesn't give her away. She silently thanks him. She shivers thinking about what lies ahead.

"How is my high liver reading?" Carol still feels the burning in her stomach from the niacin. She sees the visible symptoms of hepatitis excreted from her body. No one acknowledges her pain, including her husband.

"You are too concerned with your health," the internist checking her over responds. Carol happens to think that an inflammation of the liver, especially one that has been inflicted by a medical doctor, is something one can't ever be too concerned about.

She looks at the vents in the examining room. The fans are howling. She sits shivering, unclothed, on the cold table. The internist is reading her chart. She hates him already with a vengeance!

"I know you have a mental disorder. I just don't know which one it is yet!" the psychiatrist says. "I see you went to a poison center in Texas. That's a sure sign of a manic condition."

Carol cringes from his ludicrous statement. *My life is in his hands?* "Don't you want me to tell you what is bothering me?"

"No. From now on, we don't talk about our problems. We are here to forget what's bothering us. I myself have tinnitus. You don't see me talking about it, do you?"

Carol looks at the man holding her chart. She believes that *he* is the one with the mental condition. She just hasn't figured out which one it is yet!

"I'm afraid of anybody wearing sunglasses." Carol looks at her fellow patient in surprise. She knows that this woman definitely has a problem. But is she any different? She's afraid to walk out on the street!

Later, Carol lies curled up on her bed, glancing constantly at the nurses' station. She counts the hours until her next meal and tranquilizer time. She is afraid to refuse to attend "group." She is afraid not to pretend that she is better. The threat of being thrown upstairs in the locked unit looms heavily over her like the monster her medical condition has become.

She listens to a patient who has problems with depression. This woman is receiving electric shock treatments. Carol wishes she could trade her own problem with the depression sufferer. She hears others talk about their alcohol and substance abuse addictions. Carol knows that she is addicted to drugs also. She wants to be any of these other patients. Anyone with a diagnosable illness. Anyone who has a chance of getting well. She has none.

"Get out of my chair!" The attractive male patient is new and a mean type. Carol jumps up and looks at the chair, trying to find his name tag on it.

"You're following me around!" her psychiatrist seriously comments.

Is he paranoid?

Fred brags to everyone how Carol is now eating everything. He knows she has had to forego her organic food theories and brainwashing conditioning. He is so happy she is eating "regular" food.

The ward nurse tries to cheer her up. "I have never seen such a high liver reading in all my life!"

Fred and David visit often. Fred goes to extra lengths to bring all her favorite food treats. At least she is not going to starve to death. She is on another route.

Peanut is living in the veterinarian's kennel. Carol is living in the mental ward. Fred keeps pressuring Carol to realize that she can no longer have Peanut in their home. He refuses to care for her dog. He seems happy to be living alone. It won't be long before he always is!

"By next week, I will have you off all your drugs completely," the psychiatrist promises. "I'll allow you to have a benedryl tablet for sleep if you like."

Oh, thank you! How thoughtful!

"You will also have to take my new prescription."

Carol is horrified. Now she projects her future stay in the hospital without the aid of tranquilizers. She will be forced to swallow his antidepressant tablets, even though she is not depressed. *I'm running out of time. I have to get out of here!*

"I can lose my job if you tell anyone that I gave you another doctor's name," the helpful floor nurse says. She slips Carol the name of a specialist she herself sees.

"What's a TMJ doctor?"

"It's a dentist who can straighten your jaw if it is out of alignment. It could be the reason your teeth are ground down so much. My tinnitus is a lot better since I started this treatment."

Now Carol is really desperate. She grows more and more frantic with every breath she takes.

"I have already talked to all the hearing organizations." Carol can't seem to convince Sylvia from the phone in her cell.

"I called to help you," her friend says. Carol looks at the ward room that is now her prison. "At least talk to the doctor again." Carol finally agrees.

"Does the shower cover up your tinnitus?" This isn't the first time the Oregon Research Center doctor has asked Carol this question. She has called him, too, repeatedly, along with almost every other human being connected with tinnitus in the United States.

"No. But something is definitely different when I turn the shower off." She is afraid to use the bathroom in her hospital room, especially the shower. Why?

"You can start taking Xanax." Her shaking hand attempts to write down his instructions for the dosage. "Masking and Xanax are better than death." Somehow Carol doesn't think so as she cringes from his words.

Carol looks out the window from her ward every day, waiting and hoping. *The TMJ specialist said he would come. He has to!* She shakes at the sound of the rain beating on the hospital roof. *Where are the chunks of hail that I hear? I see only rain!*

"Close your mouth and say sixty-six." Carol is so grateful and appreciative. The TMJ specialist has left his family and work to come to the hospital through the storm. "Now count backwards from there," the wet doctor with the briefcase instructs. He has answered her prayers.

"I can't be one hundred percent sure until you come to my office for a tomogram, but I think I may be able to relieve your tinnitus."

Can he really? How wonderful!

All is still. It is the wee hours of the morning. Carol cries into the phone at the nurses' station of the psychiatric ward. "This is my solution: I need to get out of here right now! Can't you see?" she screams to Fred.

"I told you I would take you out on a full day pass next week so you can take the dental x-rays. You have absolutely no patience at all!"

Why did I marry him? Fred wants to leave me here. He scares her. *Dear God, why is this pain and unfairness happening to me? Was I such an awful person to deserve this? What did I do to deserve Fred?*

"I don't think your husband wants you back tonight," the nurse shocks Carol by saying. "He wants the doctor to okay it first. We have no authority to release you. I'm calling your doctor. He'll be here soon."

The worm is coming to get me. "You're having the psychiatrist come in at one o'clock in the morning?"

"Yes."

I don't believe this. The color drains from Carol's face. *No, this is all a mistake!*

Carol races back to her room. She grabs her jacket and purse. She flies down the hall and through the usually locked "open" door. She breathes fast, in gasps, as her hand presses the elevator button. She is too frightened to look back to see if they're coming after her. The door miraculously opens. The elevator is sitting on her floor. She presses the lobby button and pleads with God to let it close before they can get her. The thought of the locked unit upstairs weighs heavily on her tormented mind. She shakes in the elevator. *It's descending so slowly. Will they beat me to the lobby?*

The elevator comes to a halt. The doors open. She dashes through them. She pushes through the outer doors of the building. She welcomes the cool breeze on her face. It feels good. She feels free.

Carol runs through the rain toward the flashing lights of the taxi. She's lucky it's still waiting. She had placed her call before phoning Fred. She had watched the taxi arrive from her window several stories up. She had prayed it would wait. It had. *Thank you, God!*

The driver opens the back door of the cab. She jumps in. She screams, "Fast! Get me out of here fast!" The tires squeal on the pavement. She's too afraid to look back to see if they're being followed.

Chapter 13

"I have temporomandibular what? It sounds bad enough to be my problem. I sure hope it is!" Carol says to herself out loud. "I have all the symptoms. I have ringing, roaring, hissing, and buzzing in my ears, just like this medical book states. Besides this evidence, the doctor says that he can wipe out my problem."

Carol takes the tests. The TMJ specialist confirms his suspicions. "You'll have to wear these appliances twenty-four hours a day."

"I will! I will! How do I eat?"

"Very uncomfortably," her husband kids.

Her hands shake while she grinds her food in the blender. She then forces herself to ingest the mush. "I can't chew a morsel over these things."

She goes to the dental specialist's office for multiple weekly appointments. The doctor hooks her up to a machine. *So this is what biofeedback is for.* Carol is determined to overcome her anxiety and fears. The doctor tells her the machine will help her. She tells people that in three months, she will be much better. Her jaw will be in the neutral position.

"Just peel the backing from the electrodes and place them firmly on each side of your face and neck." She listens attentively as the dental technician explains the procedure of the mechanical device: "Turn on the stimulator until your eyelids and mouth involuntarily open and close by themselves."

Carol is supposed to use this "Tens machine" several times throughout the day. She is also instructed to attach it to her face thirty minutes before her appliance adjustment appointments. The machine forces her to bite down without shifting her jaw. She is to apply ice for ten minutes for severe pain and then to alternate with moist heat for twenty minutes more.

She attaches electrodes to her face and neck. She then lies in the dark trying to tolerate the horrible vibrations from the Tens machine. Her agony is unendurable. She screams out. She leaves notes to Fred that she will kill herself.

"I love you, Mommy. Please take me home," Peanut seems to be saying so clearly to Carol. Peanut's eyes light up and her tail wags as she races into Carol's outstretched arms. She has never seen her adorable dog run so fast down the hallway of the veterinary clinic.

Carol is crying as Peanut licks her over and over. Bernice says, "Hand her back now. Get it over with!"

Carol looks hatefully at Bernice. *Why am I being punished like this? I'm losing everything that I love. There's nothing to stay alive for.*

"Why aren't we going home?" her little dog seems to ask with her eyes and wiggles.

Carol is talking to Peanut like a person. She tells her that her mommy loves her more than life itself. She tells her how happy Peanut has made her through the years. She wants her dog to remember all their walks and their rides in her bike basket through town.

"Please don't forget me, Peanut." Does Peanut understand? Carol looks at the adorable animal she will never see again. Can Peanut feel how badly she is hurting?

"Peanut, I'm too sick to take care of you anymore. I don't want to give you away. I love you! I will always love you!" *Was it a mistake to hug and kiss my Peanut good-bye?* Her little dog turns her head around to look at Carol one last time as they take her away. She has a surprised, questioning look on her face. Is she imagining that look? Can dogs do that?

Carol's heart is completely shattered. She has made sure that Peanut has a wonderful home. Her new family has been searching for a companion for their own Yorkshire. Now they have one. Carol goes home sobbing, to continue dying her slow, horrible death.

She cries and cries all day long through her suffering. She cries for her lost life, for her deceased parents, for her deceased brother, and now for her little Peanut dog.

Carol is deathly afraid to go anyplace outside. She can't even go onto the patio for her morning newspaper. She dreads the shopping center where the dentist has built his new offices.

Fred jokes that her doctor's new building is being paid for by her bills. Carol thinks he's right. She finds no humor in her situation or in her life. She is cut off from the world. She is so alone.

Carol doesn't know what an MRI is. She still fights to live through her torture. She is still trying to hang onto life. She lets well-meaning professionals do whatever they want to her tortured body and mind, if they say they can help her. She is becoming more desperate. Her condition keeps getting progressively worse.

"Please remove your earplugs." Carol does what the MRI technician instructs.

Carol is in an MRI machine for the first time. Her dentist wants pictures of her TMJ joints. She feels claustrophobic in the machine. *Is a coffin similar?* She knows that no one is pounding a hammer on top of the enclosure—it just sounds like it.

"Fred, are you there? Please don't leave me!"

She asks her husband to hold her hand. Her hands are inside the machine, so he can't. Instead, he hangs onto her foot, the only part of her body that is exposed. If he lets go, she thinks she will fall apart. Fred doesn't like the noise from the machine. He uses earplugs for this activity. He's trying to be kind to his wife. Carol doesn't like this contraption one bit.

Less than a week later, Fred yells out, "Well, you finally got your wish!"

"What do you mean?"

"I just picked up a couple of your tinnitus sounds! I've got a very high-pitched screeching sound in my left ear and a high-powered, air-blasting noise in my right one. How am I supposed to sleep with all this racket? You kept saying, 'You should only have to listen to what I hear.' You wished this on me. Now I have it also! You've ruined my life!"

Fred makes Carol feel guilty for causing his problem. He theorizes that the MRI machine was the felon. He complains about noise, too! He starts to wear some of her earplugs.

Carol looks at her husband with the earplugs. He goes to his office, and he goes to his square dancing sessions. He is still able to function with this much lower level of her condition. She feels no empathy toward him. In fact, she feels now, more than ever, that his new experience should give him insight to be sympathetic to her. Fred doesn't agree.

"I think we should definitely attend the San Francisco Tinnitus Support Group," he says.

"I'd rather stay home. I already went to one of those get-togethers when this first began—remember, Fred? All I got out of it was the lemon cake that they served."

"You may not realize it, but now I have the same thing you have."

How dare he compare his condition with mine! Carol knows differently. She has been calling sufferers all over the United States. No one seems to have the extent of her symptoms. They are hurting with only a piece of what she is trying so hard to endure. *If Fred had my level of severity, he would already be dead!*

"Harriet! It's so good to see you!" Carol pulls two chairs up next to the woman she had met at last year's support meeting.

"I have tinnitus now, too," Fred announces to the group. "I try not to pay attention to it. It took me a couple of days, but I was able to adapt to it. I think it's simply a case of mind over matter."

Harriet nudges her. She whispers, "If I had a gun, I'd shoot your husband!"

That makes two of us.

"What does he think? Everyone can ignore their tinnitus?"

Harriet is angry at Fred. Carol is angry at Fred. Carol looks at Fred. He doesn't appear to be angry at all. He looks quite pleased with himself. He now has an understanding of tinnitus.

"Help me kill myself, Celia. You have to! I can't go on any longer." Carol runs into the arms of the neighbor she's so attached to.

Celia lives up the block. Celia has taken a casual "Hello, how are you?" type friendship and turned it into a commitment to help save Carol's life. She stands by Carol faithfully, like the rock of Gibraltar. Her husband Lee joins in helping, too. They incorporate Carol into their personal lives to try to save her from her impending disaster.

Celia believes the emotions Carol displays are real. She is the only friend Carol doesn't have to convince. This kind of confidence and faith is rare to find. Celia and her husband have come to Carol in her greatest hour of need. Her feelings for this couple grow along with the mystery that cannot be solved.

Carol knows she asks too much from Celia and Lee. So she occasionally cries to another nearby neighbor. "Please drive my car. Please take me to just one more doctor." She must try experimental chiropractic adjustments in Albany. Carol grew up in Albany. Now she is afraid of that city, too. Albany sounds like a jungle.

The chiropractor in Albany says, "Your first and second vertebrae are way out of alignment. No wonder this happened to you!"

"If you care about human suffering, you'll help me end this."

Celia turns white. "Come on—I'll take you up to the emergency room."

Carol obediently follows her friend. She looks up at the blinding glow from the lights at the hospital. Why aren't they comforting her like they used to? The lights always calmed her during late night visits through the parking lot. It's not safe to walk in the dark. She knows that. But now . . . she must not go near the lights. Whatever it is—it gets worse with light.

The doctor on duty is an osteopath. She had forgotten about the one in Texas until this one wrenches her neck and back. He presses strongly on her head, too. Carol is afraid. She cries. She is unaware of this doctor's treatment—there is a stronger force getting her. She once again knows it's the hospital itself. The demon is in here, but how can that be? And why?

She remembers her dying parents in beds like the one she is on. She watches the busy staff. *I need to be sick like all the others are here,* she silently pleads. *Not like I am.* She feels the needle go into her arm.

The doctor says, "This 100 milligrams of Atarax will soon put you to sleep, and you'll feel better."

He gives her prescriptions to fill. He instructs her to swallow Atarax on top of her Serax and Klonopan. Carol thinks: He's going to be a wonderful doctor, like all the others.

"You did what?" Fred yells loudly through the house. "The emergency room? What did you expect them to do for you?"

"Nothing!"

Fred asks a good question. Carol does not expect any hospital to do anything for her. They don't understand her problem. She still doesn't either.

"Now you probably won't go to Los Angeles tomorrow. You know that I went to a lot of trouble to arrange a second TMJ opinion for you there."

"I'll go. I want to talk to the TMJ surgeon."

She wants to make it clear to Fred how she can't tolerate the five to seven sounds roaring nonstop through her head. She needs help to listen to high-pitched trumpet sounds, hissing, bells ringing, noises bouncing back and forth, sounds squeaking like trains scraping on railroad tracks, and swishing noises. "I'm losing my life to this suffering, Fred!" She makes it plain as day, but to no avail.

The shot is making her sleepy. She has to withstand another trip. She is still searching for the cure. She wonders if Los Angeles will be another wild goose chase.

Carol makes it clear why she went to the emergency room the night before her trip. It hasn't been enough for Fred. She wants sympathy for her plight. She feels she deserves it. Her condition warrants it! "I called Celia because I was scared. Celia felt helpless because she couldn't do anything. She was just trying to help. I have the alarm set. I'll be ready on time."

The effects of the shot make her sleepier. *I still have to qualify my actions to Fred . . . to everyone? They don't know . . . don't understand . . . need to find out . . . still want to . . . have to live . . . don't want to leave David . . . .* She falls asleep.

Chapter 14

Carol looks at Helen, who is resting peacefully on the plane. She thinks of how little sleep she is able to get, even with a shot. She's happy Helen is going with her to the doctor in Los Angeles.

"Isn't this plane loud, Helen?"

"Not any more than usual, Carol. You know how airplanes are. You've flown just as much as I have."

Carol shudders. Will she accomplish anything at all on this trip? She's already in more pain. She's way too sick to be traveling.

"Can't you chew some vegetables?" Helen asks. Tears form in Carol's eyes. She and Helen sit in the restaurant area of the hotel in Los Angeles. She looks hungrily at the food that Helen is enjoying.

"I can't chew anything over these appliances. I'll just have to get some yogurt and cottage cheese and put it in the refrigerator." Carol is afraid to remove her TMJ splints for more than the time it takes to brush her teeth. She wears them faithfully to make her well.

"Is there a loud squealing noise here?" Carol asks the TMJ surgeon whom she has flown to Los Angeles to see.

"That's just the sound from my hearing aid."

Carol looks at the doctor who tells her that she needs her jaw joints operated on. He explains her TMJ dysfunction. She already has this information. He points to all the expensive x-rays lit up on the wall that he has just taken. They are like the others she has back home. She feels herself getting physically ill. The doctor recommends putting a surgical implant into her jaw. Her own TMJ dentist has already told her she doesn't need surgery, but he is not a surgeon. This doctor is a surgeon, and he tells her that is exactly what she does need. She is very confused.

"We don't take credit cards," the wife of the surgeon says. Carol looks at the astronomical bill just for the testing and consultation.

"May I please use your phone? I have to call my husband. I'll reverse the charges." The wife of the surgeon agrees. Carol furiously dials Fred's office.

"Fred, they won't take our credit card."

"Just write a check. Don't worry about it. I'll cover it. I made some calls. I made an appointment for you with a major specialist at UCLA. If you hurry, you can just about make it."

"Thank you, Fred!" *Maybe he does still love me.*

"Of all the nerve!" Helen mutters in disgust, as they leave. "What a racket that surgeon has going."

"He doesn't even have to hire a receptionist," Carol angrily agrees.

Carol and Helen wait. Carol prays to God that this is the doctor she has been searching for. She looks up at the kind man who tells her that he knows nothing about tinnitus. He's a cancer specialist. Her heart sinks.

"All I can do is issue an MRI order for you, but I don't think you have any tumors from what I can see. Do you want the MRI?"

She doesn't want to go into another enclosed machine, but she figures she had better do it.

She and Helen wait again. They are among a room full of strangers. *Who will hold onto me this time? We have no medical coverage for any of these bills.*

Carol is approaching almost $100,000 in medical expenses— mostly charged on credit cards. She still isn't any further along than she was from the moment her condition started. She's still not ready to give up looking for the cure though.

Here she is enclosed in another machine. This one, too, is blasting her ears into oblivion with pounding noises. The technician tells her that the doctor has just called. He wants her to have an injection of dye to double check something he has thought of. "Would you mind staying enclosed thirty minutes longer?"

She wishes she were dead. "I just want to die! Let me die!"

Carol is back home. She listens to more advice. "It can't hurt," her TMJ specialist says.

"I already tried that!" she firmly states.

"This one's awfully good. I took his classes. He uses the Chinese methods of acupuncture."

This one's not even Chinese, Carol thinks weakly.

She lies on another table with needles stuck in her earlobes, head, and face. She glances over at Helen. She can't stop the tears.

Carol does everything within her power to heal herself. She drinks Chinese herbs. She wears thick, ugly appliances. She endures the jaw pain and physical suffering of the needles. What more can she do?

She had been unable to stay in the market long enough to bag the prescribed Chinese herbs. She is progressing toward total debilitation. Only she knows . . . only she believes.

"This is going to hurt me a lot more than you," the acupuncturist with the sick sense of humor says. He inserts the long needle into the sole of her foot.

Liar!

"You have to do something," Carol sobs to the TMJ specialist. "I can't last much longer!" He does!

She looks at the long syringe filled with lidocaine. Her constant pleading is resulting in experimental trigger-point jaw injections that the TMJ doctor suggests. She doesn't worry that the injection may scar her face permanently. She's frightened that the solution won't wear off. She fears the numbing and paralyzing feeling will be with her forever.

She feels the needle piercing her jaw. "Would your wife do this?" Carol asks, as her blood splatters onto the doctor's white lab coat.

"Probably not. I just want to find the right spot." Carol listens to his words. She begins to feel sick to her stomach from what she so willingly agrees to have him do.

"Your husband will be by in a few moments," the dental assistant says, afterwards. "I called him for you."

Carol sits crying. *What else haven't I tried? Suicide?*

In the car going home, Carol can only feel swelling and numbness in her face.

"Maybe he'll have hit it right and all the noise will stop. Wouldn't that be wonderful?" she says to her husband. The car pulls up in front of their house. "Fred, I'm scared. Please, can't you come in and stay for a while?"

"What do you expect me to do? I have to get back to my office."

She doesn't know anymore how to explain comfort and emotional support. She is so frightened. She may never be able to blink her frozen eyelids again. *Can't he see what I'm doing to myself? How much longer can this insanity go on? Is this a dream? Where is that one special doctor? I need him to get me out of the grave I'm falling into.*

She goes into her house. Her face is swollen and numb. She kneels once again in prayer. *Find him, God. Please find him quickly for me before it's too late!*

Out of sheer desperation, Carol hysterically begs for several more jaw joint injections, hoping that the next one will be the charm. They all fail, of course.

"I didn't know dentists could write out prescriptions." Carol reads, " 'Tegretol, 200 mg, three times a day.' Are you sure this is safe for me to take?"

"Yes. It works on the third cranial or trigemenal nerve," her jaw joint specialist assures.

"I don't know why no one thought to give you this sooner," Ann, her pharmacist, comments. Ann eases her skepticism about the antiseizure drug. The TMJ doctor really wants her to try this.

Jim, the owner of her neighborhood drugstore, and Ann are as patient and steadfast with their help and knowledge as any two pharmacists can possibly be. These two druggists are as qualified and kind as professionals come.

Helen is again staying in Carol's home. "I've been taking Tegretol for years, since I first fainted. You don't see it hurting me now, do you?" Helen asks.

Carol looks at her friend. If she's still around, maybe she's worrying needlessly. She knows that Helen has seizures occasionally, even though she doesn't acknowledge her own condition. Helen repeatedly comes to stay with her. Carol's house and life are now a diversion.

"It's getting harder and harder to come in, Mom. Can't Helen shower? The whole house smells!"

There's a constant stench in Carol's home. She's trying to cope with it. She sees her friend's messes. She cleans Helen's clothes that are soiled. Is there anything too distasteful that she will not do to save herself?

"Helen is advancing in age, David." Carol is reaching the point of sending Helen home for good. She can no longer take care of someone else. She's barely capable of caring for herself. She forces herself to get out of bed. She asks Helen to watch her and stay by her every minute, regardless of the odors. Carol doesn't understand what is causing her to act this way. She's much too sick to know that there is a reason, a cause, and a condition.

Chapter 15

Carol is petrified! Her chest is on fire! "You've got a toxic reaction!" the jaw joint dentist says. "Stop the Tegretol at once!"

Now from her experience she knows: There is no pill on the market that touches tinnitus!

"Drink cranberry juice," a hospital emergency nurse tells Carol.

"I tried. I can't get anything down without more burning!" Carol's reactions are those of a human spirit thoroughly defeated. There really is nothing left for her to do—except die.

"Carol, I need a haircut," Helen says, coming into the bedroom. Carol has been staying in bed round the clock.

She needs a haircut and I need to die.

"Can you manage to drive us up to the corner?"

"It'll do you good." Fred pipes in with his comment.

Carol looks at her older friend. *How many more years of life does she have left? But she will outlive me!* Carol's degradation and humiliation from being debilitated are overwhelming. She wants so much to try . . . a little more . . . a little harder . . . a little longer. *Can I?*

They sit in the car in front of the beauty shop. "I can't go in there," Carol says to Helen.

"Of course you can. You're being silly."

Carol is livid with anger. "You really don't understand that I'm critically ill." She is furious and frustrated. She yells at Helen, "Do you think I'm making everything up? What do you think I've been doing these past two years, playing a game? I'm struggling to live! You of all people should be able to see that. You're living right in my home!"

"No, I know there's something wrong, but you're going to be all right!"

Obviously Helen is no longer able to assimilate effectively. Helen is out of it! Carol wants to hear someone she's close to tell her that she'll be all right. Fred does not say this. Carol's still trying to fight the growing monster. *Be brave. Don't you want Helen to like you any more? No one else does. I've lost most of my old friends.*

Carol dashes into the doorway of the beauty shop. "Can you please wash, cut and set my friend's hair? I'll be in the car." She doesn't give the owner a chance to reply.

She runs back to the car. *I did it! I made it inside!* She rolls down the window for air, pleased with herself. She looks at the trees swaying. It is exceptionally windy this May spring day. The pollen is blowing around. She removes the earplugs. "OH, GOD!" Her screams of anguish and horror blend in with what she hears.

The wind is a wailing cry. It is howling like hyenas. The earth-shattering roar sounds slurred and off-key. She's sure the tones are coming from the wind. Now she finally realizes that it doesn't matter if she wants to live more than she wants to die. It's impossible to exist. She should not try to go on. She is being forced to die. She has no choice! How and when? She still does not know!

"Call me and I'll pick you up when you're finished," Fred says.

Carol opens the car door and runs into the TMJ office. "I can't last! Nothing is working! I don't know what else I can do to save myself!" She breaks down in front of the patients and staff.

"I want you to take these Tegretol tablets and chop them up into tiny pieces," her TMJ dentist demonstrates. She watches him cutting her "poison" into fourths. "Start taking these tiny portions again immediately!"

"I got so sick from that stuff. I can't do it!"

"I really want you to."

Carol always does what the doctors really want.

Oh, God! The Tegretol is burning again. Why did I plead for help and listen to the doctor? I never should have gone back on these pills. No doctor understands what I have. I can't ingest any food now. I feel so much pain in my chest on top of my torture. This is all I need, something more to make it completely impossible to stay alive.

Carol looks through the glass of the sliding back door. Peanut's doggie doors remind her of all she has lost. Helen waves good-bye. Celia's van deafens her ears. Her friend is driving Helen back to Belmont.

Carol is alone, shaking, and drugged. Only she knows how close to death she is. Only she believes what she's experiencing is happening. All the others have long since deserted her—except Fred and David. Especially Fred. He is still here.

Carol tightly grips the 100-tablet bottle of Valium. *What if it leaves me alive and brain damaged like my mom?* She analyzes Fred. He is alive and well. He is reading the paper. She can no longer concentrate. She can no longer do anything.

95

He keeps bringing in groceries. He actually keeps her alive to suffer more. Fred does not see Carol clearly.

Carol sees Fred very clearly. "Good morning, Carol," he says, each and every day.

Only today, he doesn't see that his wife is physically different. She has metamorphosed into the beast that her condition has made her become, a very large beast with a long, long tail. She is grotesque, with bulging eyes, bared teeth encased in obtrusive plastic, and an extended tongue. She sits on several chairs pushed together in the kitchen. Her tail trails along the tiled floor.

Fred keeps reading the paper, as always, while he eats his usual breakfast. "We are out of raisins, Carol," he says, glancing up at his wife.

Carol tries to answer. She croaks her response, but he doesn't seem to notice anything different about her. He does say, though, "You look a little bloated this morning. Must have been all those beans you ate last night. Are you gaining weight all of a sudden?"

Before she can reply, he grabs the items which he has so carefully laid out the previous night. He starts out the door and then remembers to kiss his wife good-bye. "Have a nice day. Enjoy your bike ride."

Fred is no more aware of her now than he has ever been. Then her thoughts shift to her growing up days and her caring father whom Fred thought so highly of. Her deceased father's words call out to her through the incredible sounds ripping her apart.

"Carol, I want you to remember this for the rest of your life. Promise me! No matter how dim life looks, don't ever think of doing anything to end your time here. There's always a tomorrow. Tomorrow will be a new day and a new beginning. What you may want to do today might not be what you'd choose to do tomorrow. I'll always love you. I'll always be with you."

She's young, and her father is so serious. She says what he wants to hear: "I promise, Dad!"

She cries now, remembering his words. She can no longer feel much for others. Her pain overshadows everything. She stares for hours at the pills in front of her. *I love you, Dad.* She finally abides by her dad's wishes.

"This doctor said I have to get these instruments in my ears immediately, Fred. This can enable me to go on living."

"What doctor? What instruments?"

"The doctor up in Oregon at the Medical Research Center. He says that it's better to use his instruments than to die. Remember? I told you I talked to him from the mental ward. Please, I'm in so much pain. I'm pleading with you to let me do this. I need to try these things."

"You realize that we hardly have any credit left on our cards."

"I know. I'm sorry. I can't help it. I need you to come with me, to take me there."

"What? Where are you going now?" he angrily yells.

"This doctor in Oregon says to find a local audiologist. I need to get an impression of my ears. Then he can order the instruments that I should have. The doctor in Oregon says to mask my tinnitus. You know, that's like covering it up. It's supposed to drown out the sounds that are killing me with a more pleasing tone. I need to try to see if I can do this. I just thought of my dad. My parents would have wanted me to live. My brother wouldn't have wanted me to quit trying. Think about our son. What about David? He loves me. He wants to have his mother, for God's sake!"

Carol looks at Fred. She hopes she has reached him with her frantic pleas. He needs to understand the urgency of what she is telling him. He seems to.

Two weeks later, Fred and Carol leave the local audiologist with instruments that look like hearing aids. Carol wears loaners until the ones that the Oregon doctor suggests will arrive. She wears thick splints in her mouth from the TMJ dentist. Now she has things in her ears that make her look like she can't hear.

In the car, she cries and talks to Fred at the same time. "I do appreciate all you're doing for me. I drove the first time to the audiologist without bothering you. The girl with my name, Carol, is so sweet and kind. I could hardly sit still. I was sobbing so much. The audiologist tested me with awful sounds. Carol held my hand. I was so scared. I had to sit with silicone stuff in my ears for the molding impressions. The tinnitus was unbearable! You never believe me when I tell you anything," she blurts out to Fred.

"It's not a matter of believing you. The point is that you have to learn how to adapt. That's what I'd do!"

"But I know there is something wrong with these ear things. Every time your foot touches the accelerator, they make a high-pitched squeal that is deafening. Why won't you turn around and take me back there? Don't you want to help me?"

"If I didn't want to help you, would I still be here? Look what I've gone through for the past two years! No one understands how I could still be living with you!"

"I can't help what I'm doing. It's not my fault!" She looks out the window with fear. "Why are you stopping here?" She is doubled over crying.

"They have nice produce and the prices are better. After all, we're not exactly rich now! The instruments you are already complaining about are going to cost a couple of thousand more when they come in!"

Carol looks at the large chain supermarket that opened before her condition came on. Everything looks strange, off-limits.

"Are you coming in?" Fred hops out and slams the door with a thunderous bang.

"Wait! Wait for me! Don't leave me alone in the car. I'll go with you into the store. I need you to stay right by me!"

Inside, she says, "Oh, my gosh. The instruments are acting the same from the lights above the produce as they did in the car." Fred ignores her complaint. He moves methodically from vegetable to vegetable. He makes his careful selections. Carol stays right next to him.

"Don't these little tomatoes look nice?" he asks.

Carol knows it's useless to argue with him. She is so tired and exhausted. Every item in the store appears to be alive and beckoning. She shudders with horror! Her struggle with Fred is as difficult as the condition she tries to fight. He has bought her the instruments, but she still feels resentful toward him. She stays close to him out of fear. From what? She still has no idea.

At home, she cries, "The bathroom light just caused the same reaction. These machines are going berserk when they come in contact with any kind of power!" Carol is terror-stricken. She is sure the instruments are malfunctioning—just like she is!

Chapter 16

"Hi, my name is Jim. Do you have tinnitus?" a man's voice asks.

"Yes. I'm really sick! I'm going to die from it!" Carol starts to cry. She cries to someone she doesn't even know.

"Oh, my God, really?"

"Who are you? How did you get my number?"

"Harriet gave it to me. I live in Marin County. I'm going crazy with this tinnitus. I want to find out what you're doing about yours."

What haven't I done! "Harriet?—Oh, Harriet, from the support group in San Francisco." Harriet's image registers: *the woman who wants to kill my husband.* Carol wonders why she can't smile at that silly thought. She just cries and cries nonstop.

She listens patiently as Jim rattles off familiar names of doctors and treatments. "I got this blasted noise from my girlfriend's acupuncturist. She urged me to take a treatment. She ruined my life!"

Carol, in her mind, substitutes "tinnitus" for "she." The affliction does the ruining.

"I've tried everything," he finally says.

You haven't heard anything yet! She vividly paints a picture of her condition and plight.

"Oh, my God!" he keeps repeating, the more she divulges. "You poor thing! I would already be dead!"

"I am dead. I don't even have a friend left!"

"Well, you do now! What do you look like?" Jim wants to know.

Suddenly, Carol thinks she might still care how she looks. "I have these thick, ugly appliances in my mouth. I just started wearing instruments in my ears that squeak all the time. I cut off all my long hair so I can take quick showers. People used to say I was cute before all this, but I'm really awful looking now. I was working in the fashion industry, too."

She paints him an accurate picture of herself. When she looks in the mirror she doesn't recognize the reflection. She feels like Dracula with mouthpieces, and now Dumbo, too, with ear devices!

"How tall are you? How much do you weigh?" the obvious ladies' man asks.

"I'm five-foot-four and pretty skinny! I was just given a terrible drug that's causing me stomach problems!"

"No kidding? I have stomach problems, too!"

Carol listens to a familiar description of the same route she has traveled seeking tinnitus help. She hears his anger, frustration, and explicit vocabulary that she, too, now uses regarding the medical profession. Her mother frowned on swearing. Carol no longer cares. She closes her eyes while Jim puts down the help in the Bay Area. Her mother's voice returns, *"Ooh, how can you watch all those scary movies? You'll wake up screaming and have nightmares for the rest of your life!"* She had thought that her mother's sentiments were ridiculous then. Now—she should only know!

"I have the name of a doctor who reportedly has patients who, after his treatment, don't hear any tinnitus!" Jim's statement jars Carol back to his conversation with a jolt.

"You dooo? Honest?"

"Yes, and I have paperwork on his technology. I'll bring the information for you, if you want to get together and meet me someplace."

"Yes, of course I do! That sounds wonderful!" *It sounds too good to be true.* "God, thanks! Thank you so much!" *How am I going to meet him when I'm afraid to leave the house?*

"How'd you hear of this doctor?" *Could this be real?*

"I've been calling around to other patients since I came down with this blasted noise. A guy gave me his name."

"What guy?"

"I don't remember—oh, someone down South."

"My God! You're calling patients, and I've been calling doctors. I need this doctor's name and information right away!"

"Listen, it's Sunday. You can't do anything today. Can you meet me in Berkeley tomorrow, at around noon?"

"Where?"

"Do you know Berkeley?"

"Yes. I grew up near there." *But I'm afraid of that city, too. That would go over really big.*

"What about in the parking lot at Whole Foods? I'm driving a red truck."

"I have a black Honda SI. How will I know you?"

"I'm tall and thin. I'm letting my hair grow long. All the girls think I'm good looking!"

Carol grips the steering wheel. She tries to draw on all the courage and strength she once had. The oncoming cars resemble jet planes as she struggles to keep her foot on the accelerator. She repeatedly alternates between flipping the air conditioner on and off. She opens and closes the window. Whatever is outside has to remain there. She tries hard to concentrate on driving safely. The car radio and cassette player contribute to the force that is dragging her down. She snaps the power off.

Carol has no idea what is happening. The trees swaying in the spring breeze hiss like thousands of snakes. The birds squawking en masse take over the sky and the earth. When she looks out the window, she sees nothing unusual. She can't see the force that she hears so loudly. The entire environment howls into the bowels of the earth.

Carol removes the ear pieces and shoves earplugs into her ears. She leaves the appliances in her mouth. She glances into her car mirror to see if she looks better than she feels. She cringes with horror as she gets out of her car. The air hits with a blast of volume.

A tall fellow approaches. "Jim?" He nods and they hug briefly. They sit at an outdoor table getting to know one another.

"Do you think I'm good looking?"

I'm dying and he's asking about his looks! Jim catches her off guard. "Yes." *Who is he?*

He smiles. They quickly form an easy rapport.

"I need to make a decision about the women in my life."

She ignores his comment. "Let's see the information you have about the doctor." Jim hands her his fax printouts. Nothing else matters to Carol except the doctor and his data.

She glances over the sheets. She's astonished that both Dr. Pawel J. Jastreboff and the treatment sound concrete. There is documented proof on everything she reads. This doctor was even on television.

Jim points out, "He uses instruments like yours. If you're going to all the trouble and expense of buying and wearing those things, you might as well have the ones that get rid of the tinnitus."

Jim's a lot smarter than I am. He finds out everything from patients while I fall flat on my face with the doctors.

"Are *you* planning on wearing them?"

"You can tell me what they do for you first," he says laughingly.

Carol looks at her very clever friend. "I have to rush home and see if I can get this doctor on the phone, Jim. Just say a prayer for me, okay?"

"You're going to be all right, kiddo!" He gives her a hug good-bye.

"You can be my brother," she says, thinking of her own brother, gone forever. Carol wipes away the tears that trickle from her eyes.

"You got it!" he happily replies.

Carol shudders with anxiety as she starts up her engine. The car moves up the street. She looks over at the Claremont Hotel off Ashby Avenue where she and Fred spent their honeymoon night. *Please, dear God, I have no more time. Please make this doctor be the correct one. If he isn't, I won't live. I need him to be nice. Just make him be nice and make him help me. I have no one else to turn to. My life depends on this man! Please make this be my lucky day!*

"Tinnitus and Hyperacusis Center," a woman's voice announces. Carol tries to steady herself.

"Hello? I'm calling from California. I need to speak to Dr. Jastreboff—please. It's an emergency!"

"Just one moment." Carol is astonished. *Just like that! Something's wrong. It's too easy! Just let him come on the phone,* she prays.

"Hello. This is Dr. Jastreboff."

"My name is Carol, and I need your help really badly. I'm dying from tinnitus, and I don't know what to do. Please help me! I've so many sounds, and they keep repeating. They're so loud." Carol's whiny voice changes into a fast, sobbing recitation. "I'm so scared! I don't want to die! I've already probably wrecked my ears. I put DMSO down them and also a lidocaine mixture. I got poisoned. I put all these chemicals on my hair and then I went into the swimming pool which wasn't balanced right. I went to a poison center. I got overdosed with niacin. I'm swallowing so many pills. I even had my jaw moved over. Please, can you help me?" She is unaware that she is crying.

The doctor sounds puzzled as she hears him reply, "Well, yes. Do you have a hearing test?"

"Oh, yes, yes. I have a lot of them."

"I only need one."

"Which one? I'll send you all of them!"

"Do you have the latest one?"

"Yes, I have it! I have a fax machine. I can fax it to you this minute—right now. Is that okay? Will you please look at it?"

"Yes, that's fine."

"Can I call you back? I need to get your exact instruments. I have an audiologist here. Can you tell him what I need so I can get them right away? Can you do that? Is this possible?"

"Yes!"

"You'll help me then?"

"First, I need to look at your hearing results. You can make me a list of your symptoms."

"Thank you. Thank you so much! I really appreciate it! I'm going to fax it right this second to you. It's going to come out on your machine there right now! Are you sitting near your fax machine? Will you be there to get it?"

"Yes, I'll get it."

"Thank you! Thank you so much! I really appreciate it. I can't thank you enough!"

"All right."

"Thank you. God bless you! Good-bye."

"Good-bye," Dr. Jastreboff finally gets a chance to say.

"**H**ello, Jim? I didn't know if you would be home yet. Guess what? That doctor you gave me. He's nice! He says he'll help me!"

"Really now? That's great! He came on the phone?"

"Yes, Yes! I just talked to him!"

"No kidding? Did you call him at his home?"

"No, I didn't call him at his home! I called his office. Then I faxed him my hearing test."

"No fooling. I want him to look at mine, too. Do you suppose he will?"

"Probably. He's reading mine right now. I also don't know what to do about these instruments that the Oregon Medical Research Center recommends. They keep making horrible squeaking noises. I know Fred thinks they are fine. He never believes me when I tell him what's wrong. I need to get the correct ones now from someone who is following Dr. Jastreboff's treatment."

"Well, I believe you, kiddo. Why don't you get the generators from the doctor I saw at the medical center in San Francisco? I know he goes to the same American Tinnitus Association seminars that Dr. Jastreboff goes to."

"Is the medical center doctor nice?"

"He is to me."

"Oh, I wish I had your problem, Jim!"

"You're going to be fine, kiddo. Hang in there!"

Chapter 17

"I'm bundling up so much from this condition, Fred. Look how many sweaters I wore today. Now I'm sweating in the car."

Fred doesn't answer. He's busy driving Carol to buy the correct generators.

Carol removes her jacket and top sweater. Her eyes close. She's exhausted from the drugs and lack of sleep. Now she has a chance of getting well. There's hope once again on the horizon. *Maybe I won't die. I can't! I don't want to! I want to see and do so much more. I wonder if everyone dying feels this way.*

She thinks of her brother. She is so weary. She opens her eyes to look at Fred. *Such a horrible fight to live.* The movement of the car causes her eyes to close again. It lulls her into a light sleep. . . .

She is back to a time before her illness. She is going to a luncheon on a gorgeous, sunny day. She wears one of her pretty lightweight outfits, suitable for the weather.

She is laughing. She adjusts the air conditioner and radio in the car. She is happy.

Carol opens her eyes, hears the thunderous noise, and knows that this is her fate. First she feels hot, then shaky and cold. Her teeth clatter from nerves. Her eyes twitch from anxiety. Her chest burns, and everything she eats seems to come back up in her throat. She is a total mess. She feels like a freak and knows she is an oddity of nature's cruelest suffering, dished out to her in a portion too large to handle.

Tears stream down her face as she looks longingly out the window at the streets of San Francisco. She loves the City. She remembers everything in the past that she now fears and can't do.

"Boy, am I hungry!" Fred says. They walk across the underground parking lot of the major medical center, looking for an elevator.

"Don't leave me alone for a minute, please!" She hears the cement echo their footsteps with the force of a dinosaur. "I'm so afraid! I hope I make it through the day!"

"Can't I go eat something?" Fred pulls Carol toward a luncheonette.

"No, I can't stop anywhere else. Can't you see that?"

No one else can see—or hear—the evil lurking about her.

"Your wife is so sick," the attractive employee comments, after one look at Carol. "I'll try to hurry your paperwork through. I'm afraid you don't qualify for the reduced rate that our medical center offers."

Carol loves the gorgeous outfit the young woman is wearing. *I used to wear pretty clothes. I used to look decent.* She wants her life back so badly. In addition, she knows what her medical expenses are doing to their finances.

She thinks of herself as a walking corpse with funny-looking, thick appliances cutting into her teeth and gums. Now she is adding instruments around her ears to enhance her ghoulish image. She intends to explain all of these negative feelings to the doctor in this building.

"**N**o wonder you're hearing squeaking sounds. You have nothing but a pair of old hearing aids in your ears. I'm hearing them squeal, too," the doctor at the medical center states.

Carol gives Fred a see-I-told-you-so look. She hopes now Fred will believe her more. The doctor examines her ears.

"You have swimmer's ears. Do you swim a lot?"

"Yes, I sure do. Well I *did* is what I mean." She's beginning to think that this San Francisco doctor really knows ears. "Can you please call Dr. Jastreboff and get me the very same model of these instruments that he uses?" She dares to hope that this machinery will give her a chance to recover like Dr. Jastreboff's paperwork states so plainly. Carol begins to cry uncontrollably.

"I can, but if you think you're going to benefit by wearing these generators with your behavior the same as it is now, you're wasting my time and yours. You won't get any good out of these instruments, and I don't really want patients like you." Carol had been crying in the waiting room, too. But then she cries every place all day and all night.

"She won't even let me go to the bathroom alone." Fred reinforces the doctor's viewpoint. Carol is hurt and angry. She thinks over her response carefully.

"I'll try to do better," she deliberately forces herself to say. *This doctor may not even get me the generators that just may save my life. I'd better pretend to act nice and not cry hysterically.*

"Here—use these until the new ones come in." The doctor hands instruments to her. "They are both the same brand. One is just an older model than the other."

"Are the tones the same?" she asks anxiously.

"They should be close enough for a short time."

Carol looks at her two opponents in the room. She can't defend herself. Everything they say about her is true, but she can't help it! She can't control herself! Why?

Carol is once again cringing in the underground garage. She tries to keep up with Fred's fast stride. "He isn't nice! I don't like him, but I want those generators! I'm only seeing him because I think he knows Dr. Jastreboff." She starts to cry. "I really need to go to Baltimore for the correct doctor and his generators, Fred. I'm only getting them here because I know I'm too sick to make it back East. I can hardly sit in the car to even come here. I can barely walk on the street anymore." Carol needs Fred's understanding so badly. And she needs the Baltimore doctor more than she's needed any person in her entire life. *Please, God, help me with this doctor back East!*

She is alone. She will have to try to make the Eastern doctor help her all by herself. Can she do it, and what kind of a person is he?

In the car driving home Fred says, "I sure hope these new instruments make you act like this doctor said you should. I can't take much more of this!"

He keeps saying that. What about me?

"Dr. Jastreboff really is something else, Fred. Can you imagine what Jim did? He put the three of us on a joint conversation. It wasn't even Jim's phone, and to the doctor's house on a Sunday. Dr. Jastreboff is so patient and kind sounding. Any other doctor would have been furious. He sounds as wonderful as his treatment does."

"That's nice."

Carol has not caught Fred's attention, as usual, with her important information. She is still fighting for Fred's help to keep her alive. She doesn't know that her biggest struggle is still ahead. She's so frantic and desperate to catch this one special doctor's attention. Her intuition tells her that this doctor is the only reason she is still living.

Carol starts writing. Her hand shakes as she puts "Not Human Suffering" at the top of her paper. She no longer thinks she is human. Next she writes "Chart of My Problems." She describes: "Excruciating pain in my ears; beeping and humming noises, almost like music; winding projector sounds; hissing and gurgling water sounds; high-shrill screeching; changing tones, like violins playing; and trumpet staccato beats. All the sounds in the house pulsate up and down. The sounds change in velocity but are never low in volume."

She cries as she faxes. Dr. Jastreboff faxes right back.

She refaxes. He responds again. She calls. He talks to her. She leaves a phone message. He quickly returns the call. The kind and conscientious voice that never fails to give Carol's repeated calls and faxes to her boss belongs to Donna Earling of Baltimore, Maryland, his office assistant.

Carol digs through her albums. She cries through her mission. She finds two perfect photographs.

In the first, she sits at an outdoor table in Paris without a care. The bottle in front of her is marked Lemon Concentrate. Her stomach burns from everything now. Carol remembers drinking undiluted acidic lemon all the time then.

In the second, she poses on skis high on the mountain, ready to conquer the run. This picture shows a beautiful snow peak in the Alps.

Carol hopes that Dr. Jastreboff will love her two pictures. He is from Europe. She loves Europe. Already she loves him, too!

Carol watches the San Francisco doctor and his staff eating chocolate cake. She can no longer eat without problems. She wonders why the employees don't have tinnitus. They are not eating organic food. In fact, they are eating junk food. She used to love junk food.

"Can you please give me a hair cell test?" she asks the medical center doctor.

He looks very surprised that she knows these things. He hesitates. "Okay." He doesn't ask her how she knows. Carol's source is Jim. The doctor gives her the test. She observes the printout. She wants it.

"May I please have my results?"

"No!" The doctor is definite.

"There's something really bad, isn't there?"

"Your reaction is precisely the reason I didn't want to do this test!"

Carol gets the correct generators though. She is confident her test results will be forthcoming, too. *The very nerve! Medical records belong to the patient! I know that!*

At home, Carol angrily calls the medical center doctor and boldly states, "I need to fax my hair cell test results to Dr. Pawel J. Jastreboff."

She smiles as she watches the results come out of her fax machine almost immediately. She hopes that the San Francisco doctor knows now who's working with her!

Carol calls Baltimore to ask for data on Dr. Jastreboff's program. She looks at the paperwork emerging from her fax machine "Instrumentation and Tinnitus: A Neurophysiological Approach" by Pawel J. Jastreboff. She glances up at her kitchen clock. The noise of the second hand moving resembles the sound of firecrackers exploding. It is past midnight. She figures out the late hour time change in Baltimore as she silently thanks God and Dr. Jastreboff for caring!

She reads rapidly. Her eyes focus in on one section of his paper that is entitled "A New Tinnitus Treatment Protocol Brings Hope to Millions." She finds what she is in a frenzy to understand—TRT (Tinnitus Retraining Therapy). "The process takes eleven to eighteen months to where the patient is no longer aware of tinnitus a majority of the time, or not at all." Carol reads further that patients usually discontinue wearing the white noise generators.

All right! Way to go! She is thrilled! She can live! She will get well! She doesn't have to die! She has hope now. She has help now—she doesn't know if she has enough strength now!

Something has changed. The generators make the tinnitus better, but the sinister force that scares her is worse. It has grown, along with more terror than a human being can stand!

She looks at the generators. They are pieces of machinery that look like hearing aids. They run on batteries. There is a dial with numbers to set. Carol has to turn the dial to increase and decrease the broadband frequency sound that the instruments make. She is told that it is a very gentle sound, barely audible. It isn't though. Something is very wrong! The sound is increasing and decreasing all by itself. She is not touching the dial. It's the inexplicable force again. It's always there, pushing her a little closer to the edge.

Can Dr. Jastreboff save her? Or is this the devil himself, and it's already too late? She needs these answers. She has to know!

Chapter 18

"I can't live! I can't hold out! Please help me!" she screams into the phone to Dr. Jastreboff.

Carol hears his voice calmly say, "Keep the generator noise below the level of your tinnitus, always. You do not want to cover up the tinnitus with the generator noise."

"I can't! It doesn't work right! The generator dial is shifting all by itself! They're so loud. I can't stand them! I try to turn them down, but then they go back up automatically. The dial moves all by itself. They sound like a motorboat running. I know what that sounds like—I used to water ski." Her screams turn into uncontrollable sobs, as she cries her heart out to the doctor back East.

"You just need time now. Be patient!"

She hears his voice. He is calm. He is so matter-of-fact. He states so confidently, so assuredly, that she will be fine someday. But when? And what about now?

Carol feels dead. She wants to feel life. She needs to know she's alive, so she asks, "Can I go to a wedding?"

Dr. Jastreboff says, "Yes!"

"What do I do about the noise?"

"Wear earmuffs that reduce sound over the generators."

His answers are explicit. She somehow knows that he will always say "yes" to things she wants to do. He is kind. He wants people to enjoy life. He wants her to be well and happy. He really wants to help her. She needs to try.

Fred and Carol go to the wedding. It's for Sylvia's daughter, Debbie. Carol really wants to go if she can survive it.

"Your dress looks cute." Fred drives on the freeway.

"You better take me home! Please!" She removes the headset and then puts it back on. She is trapped in the car, as Fred ignores her pleas. He continues driving to the wedding. *Sylvia is my friend. Fred just wants to go eat.*

At the wedding, Carol cries in front of dressed-up people. She cries because she's afraid of the building she's attempting to enter. Everyone is staring at her with the headset decorating her head. Fred tries to ignore her. She hesitantly walks near the man who is talking to Fred. His voice scares her, like the other people do who enter the building. Everything seems too noisy.

"Where are you going, Fred?"

"To get some hors d'oeuvres and a drink in the little room over there."

Carol follows him. She notices that the small room is an impossibility. She sees a wet bar. The activities look familiar and standard for the occasion. People mill around, sampling the food and drinks. They talk and laugh. She is hysterical and in agony. There are no distinguishable sounds in the small area. Everyone's movements are running together in one unbearable, jumbled loudness of death. *Where can I run to? Why can't someone rescue me?*

"I'm going into the main dining room, Carol, to look for our seats." She is hurt by his indifference to her pain. She wants to tell him to die, like she is doing.

Instead, she answers, "Don't leave me! Wait—I'll come with you!"

She looks at the people talking at her table. Her junior high school friend's husband says, "Carol, how are you? Gee you look great!"

She thinks she looks great, too—so great all dressed up that she can go directly into her casket!

"Have some water," Fred says, as she watches him smearing butter on his bread. She looks at the lemon floating in the water. She swallows her saliva, but it burns.

I wonder how a crumb of bread would feel going down. I'm afraid to find out! "I have to go home, Fred! Now! This instant! I can't stand anything here, especially the music, even with the headset!"

"Go out to the car. It will be quiet there. I just want to finish my dinner!"

Carol runs outside, sobbing. She can't find quiet anyplace. She runs back into the building. Sylvia grabs her arm. "Stand here, Carol."

Four friends from teenage days stand together for the photographer. The other three are old friends who are alive. She is a ghost who tries to smile. She expects the developed picture to depict only three women.

"They're going to cut the cake," Fred says.

Carol wonders how she can be attending a wedding when she feels like she is no longer living in the world.

"**W**hat is an electroencephalograph report and a carotid artery test?" She needs to know.

Everyone knows what an upper GI series is. Carol never has had one. She can't eat without pain. She needs these tests. She forces herself to go beyond her capabilities to take them. The results are negative, the same as all her other tests. She hopes to heal her digestive tract with the correct medicine. She doesn't know she needs the right doctor before she can get the right medicine.

"The Zantac is not touching my esophagus problem!" she tells her local internist. She cries into a tissue in front of him. She already knows the look of disbelief. She hates all doctors. She will never forgive them. *He doesn't believe me either!*

"Go to your sink," Dr. Jastreboff instructs.

"Don't leave me!" she cries, as she grips the portable phone.

"I'm right here. Now turn on the water."

"Niagara Falls. I've got a Niagara Falls in my sink!" she screams out, horrified.

Carol shakes with fear, but knows she is safe. Dr. Jastreboff is hanging onto her from Baltimore, Maryland.

"Now shut it off and tell me what you hear."

"It's a lot quieter."

"Good," he says. "You should habituate quite nicely."

What does he mean?

She loves to talk on the phone. She admits she is a "phonoholic." Jim begins to place her on conference calls.

"Hello, Dan? This is Jim."

"Hi, Jim. What's up?"

"I've a friend on the line. Say hello, Carol, to Dan Malcore in Wisconsin."

"Hi, Dan." The three of them talk. Dan runs a hyperacusis network. He compiles a bulletin. Carol's horizons are broadened. She receives her first *Hyperacusis Bulletin*.

"There seem to be hundreds of people on Dan's mailing list." She pushes the *Hyperacusis Bulletin* directly in front of Fred's face to get his attention. "There's a woman who lives in San Francisco, Arabella Colton," Carol excitedly says. "I'm planning to call her." She desperately needs a friend close by. Maybe this woman can encourage her to stay alive. "This condition doesn't discriminate in its victims. There's an MD sufferer on this network. I know there are afflicted movie stars, but how can they make pictures while I'm dying here?" She doesn't wait for her husband's response. "I guess everyone who has this is affected differently."

Fred's brow deepens with a frown. She doesn't think he's listening to her. He's busy reading parts of the bulletin, too. He grabs his calculator. She watches his fingers begin to fly over the keys. "Hmmm. . . . There're a lot of people suffering from various levels of what you have, Carol. According to statistics, ten to twenty percent of the general population have tinnitus. That's as high as one billion people in the world. But wait . . . about four to five percent of the general population have problems because of it . . . so that's two hundred and fifty million people in the world suffering from tinnitus!"

"My gosh! Oh, my gosh! Two hundred and fifty million people who probably don't know what to do. They could be helped by this treatment." She runs to the den to find her faxes from Baltimore. "Dr. Jastreboff states here, see. . . ." She points her finger on the literature she tries to assimilate in her tortured, noise-filled mind: "Hyperacusis is the other side of the coin with tinnitus. My God! I must have this other thing, too!"

Carol continues to read to herself. She screams out, "A gain in the auditory system? The volume is turned up? How much volume? But I have perfectly normal hearing! If I don't have any hearing loss, oh, my God! Every time my auditory system comes in contact with a noise, no matter how minute it is, the noise is magnified! Oh, dear God! Dear God in heaven!"

She sits down on the carpet in total shock. "This thing devastates everyone in its path and leaves destruction in its wake! It's evil! It's the devil incarnate! It squeezes life out of its victims!"

"Get a hold of yourself, Carol. You're so dramatic!" She waits for any sign of sympathy. Fred continues, "I'm sorry you're so bad off. This throws a different light on everything."

Will Fred be kind now?

"Why don't all these millions of people go to Dr. Jastreboff? Why didn't I?" She again answers without Fred's response.

"Oh!" She puts her hands over her face and shakes her head from side to side. "I was so stupid! I should have figured out the hyperacusis part. No wonder I was scared of everything. Oh, my God! I should have found Dr. Jastreboff from the beginning! I'd be well by now! His information is so mixed in with the others' stuff that it's impossible to figure out what's the right thing to do. I'll never be able to forgive myself! He was here all the time. I just wasn't able to see it!" She is completely devastated.

"Who was where?"

"Dr. Jastreboff! Aren't you listening at all?"

"It's kind of hard not to!"

Carol ignores Fred's sarcasm. *"Just ignore him,"* her mother would say. *"He doesn't know any better. He'll say he's sorry. That's more than your father will do."*

She used to laugh at all her mom's philosophies. She misses her mother. She knows her mom didn't mean to be difficult. Carol realizes that her mom's mini-strokes changed her actions and personality. "I didn't understand," she wishes she could say, but she doesn't get a second chance. *Will there be any second chances for me?* Carol continues her monologue to Fred on Dr. Jastreboff.

"He was written up in the March 1994 *Tinnitus Today* quarterly. It says he was on CNN. That was in 1992, before I came down with this. How could we have overlooked him? I remember when you read the write-up in the ATA quarterly, Fred. You said, 'Do you want to wear things in your ears like some of these people are doing?' "

"Carol, we thought you had gotten poisoned at the time. And besides, you couldn't even stand the sound from the wave machine I bought you. How quickly they forget." Fred's words ring true.

She remembers crying in the store and mall over the wave machine. Her recent wedding fiasco comes to mind. Everything starts to make sense, all her weird and bizarre actions. Is it too late?

"See, you never believed me! No one did. The doctors still think I'm mentally deranged. My friends think I just went to sleep one night and woke up a raving lunatic the next morning. You think I should be handling tinnitus better." She doesn't give Fred a chance for a rebuttal. She thinks he doesn't deserve it.

"I just realized I'm in a 'catch-22.' When I put the headset on over the generators to block the magnified outer sounds, the stupid tinnitus is being brought in louder. This condition is unlivable, Fred. It's totally unlivable!" Her voice turns to sobbing as she desperately tries to evoke some sympathy from Fred. Fred sits reading.

"I have weird, pulsating tinnitus that's interacting with the outside sounds. When the tinnitus bounces back and forth like drums beating away, every sound that's running straight, like water, or static on the television, car engines—there have to be a million sounds around like that: airplanes, wind, rain, the refrigerator—I hear all these straight noises magnified, doing the same beating as the tinnitus. Now you tell me if I don't have a good excuse for my actions! Can you think of anything else on earth more terrifying and torturous?"

Fred shakes his head sympathetically.

Carol finally has his attention. "The sounds are a thousand times as loud as normal. That's bad enough by itself, but no, I have to endure blasting bongo drums as well. My auditory system plays the tinnitus sounds and then throws them into the outside noises. Then it plays them all back to me excruciatingly loud, slurred, and off-key. How would you like to have a copycat like that in your head? How could you stay alive with this? Can you answer me that? How long could anyone stay alive with this?"

She knows what Fred's answer would be regarding living with her condition. She can't hear it verbalized if she hopes to make it through Dr. Jastreboff's treatment. Fred looks compassionately at Carol. She wants to make sure he understands what she's trying to deal with.

"The awful tinnitus beats keep changing in velocity and rhythm. They seem to echo one another. I hear **boom boom**

boom boom one day, and then **b'boom b'boom b'boom b'boom** the next."

"Will you stop making those noises! They're very annoying and you're giving me a headache doing that!"

"I'm just trying to demonstrate so you'll understand how bad off I am." Carol wants to cry in his arms. She wants Fred to say, "You'll be all right now with Dr. Jastreboff helping you."

Instead, she hears, "I'm sorry. I know how bad off you are."

He doesn't know. It's impossible for him to know what he can't experience. "All these past years, I've been doing horrible, detrimental things to my body. I had enough torture from this awful condition without adding to it. I just couldn't figure it out. If only I could have realized what it was, it would be over by now. Instead, I'll probably never make it. It's humanly impossible! I have an unlivable tinnitus and hyperacusis condition! You have to know that, Fred!"

"How can anyone know such a thing without experiencing it?"

"Dr. Jastreboff knows!" she screams angrily. "The doctors are supposed to know! People are supposed to know! The whole world needs to know! The medical profession is supposed to believe Dr. Jastreboff! What happened to me is an inhumane atrocity! How many sufferers are going to commit suicide before people become aware of these afflictions? It doesn't have to be this way. Isn't change what living is all about? People can be educated to recognize these afflictions. They need to know what causes them, and how to prevent them."

"I agree with you, Carol. Calm down and let it rest for a while."

She finally becomes quiet. She is all talked out for the time being. She finally makes her point with Fred. Now she just has to live. Carol finally understands what she's been dealing with. The monster has a name: "Hyperacusis." Except . . . this treatment . . . something is very suspicious about it. There's something going on with the generators that Dr. Jastreboff knows, but she doesn't. Carol thinks he realizes she doesn't understand, but she thinks he wants to keep it this way. Why? He's so honest and forthright. Maybe all Carol's supposed to know is that she has to stay alive and keep on with his treatment.

Can she conquer this? She doesn't think it's possible to survive the magnitude of what she has. Is this what Dr. Jastreboff thinks and is afraid to tell her? Is she going to die anyway? *Oh, God, please don't let me die! Not after I've finally found the one doctor in the world who can bring me back.* Her thoughts cause her to sob. Fred has said he's sorry. Is this supposed to fix everything? Is this supposed to make her live again? She still doesn't feel empathy from him. She only feels it from Dr. Jastreboff— Dr. Jastreboff and David. She feels so isolated and so alone. She has too much time ahead with too much suffering. It's a slow process—it moves like a snail.

Am I going to make it? Is Dr. Jastreboff going to make sure I do? It already seems that way. Such a wonderful, dear man. He's going to try his best to pull me through, no matter what, against all unbeatable odds. Carol looks over at Fred.

Chapter 19

"Now I have it! I can't stand the high-pitched music at my square dances anymore. And your voice—that's the very worst sound!"

Carol is mad at everything Fred says. First, he equates his condition with hers. Then it's her voice that bothers him. How can he compare his condition to hers? It's like comparing apples and oranges. But she doesn't dare tell him this. She needs him to stay. That is what is important. If there's a chance to survive Dr. Jastreboff's treatment, she needs to give it her all.

She's getting the treatment from the generators, but it's a slow, painful process. Her digestive tract has been severely irritated, too. Can she bear up to this level of suffering to give the generators a chance to tone down the sounds? Carol hopes she can. She prays Fred will grow to be more sympathetic in time—assuming she lives that long!

Carol listens to Jim. He evaluates the difference between his and her condition. "If you had what I have, you'd be dancing pirouettes. What you need, kiddo, is a good orthomolecular doctor like mine. My MD says he's going to knock out my tinnitus with his health regimen."

That's impossible! It sure didn't work for me! He almost killed me with a niacin overdose! Carol doesn't verbally dispute Jim's beliefs. She knows from her own experience that orthomolecular treatments won't help tinnitus.

Carol telephones Arabella. She sounds sympathetic and understanding. Arabella has to wear earplugs to put up with her sound intolerance. They discuss the afflictions and agree that doctors in the San Francisco Bay Area are misinformed and mistrained in their treatments.

Arabella has a functional level of hyperacusis that she wants to reverse. She believes in Dr. Jastreboff. She plans to be his patient also. Carol and Arabella decide to stay in touch by telephone. And they do, too!

She has connected with a strong support figure. Arabella's kind words will influence her to hang on through the torture she cannot stand. Arabella will be there for Carol, who will be grateful forever.

Carol begins to doubt that Jim believes her. "How are the generators doing?" he asks every day.

"It's too soon to tell." Jim causes her to think, what if the generators don't work? This is not like swallowing an antibiotic for an infection. Carol must reduce her anxiety, not increase it! She needs positive thinking. The generators work off the brain. She wants to give herself every opportunity to allow the generators to work. She surmises what Jim thinks. Now she listens to and believes only Dr. Jastreboff from 3,000 miles away. She admires her doctor's integrity and ideals. The doctor is honest and sincere.

When Fred asks, "How's Jim?" she responds by adopting Dr. Jastreboff's exact words and sentiments:

"I can't force people to believe. Everyone is entitled to their own opinions."

Carol wonders if Jim, like many others, thinks that only doctors with stethoscopes save lives. Why not? She did. She hadn't given Dr. Jastreboff's Ph.D. much thought. She was too sick. She needed to grab onto any chance for help.

Now she learns from hindsight. Ph.D.s do research. They develop treatments and cures for humanity. They eradicate disease and bring miraculous hope to the world. They work from grants and foundation endowments. They allow medical doctors to gain advanced technology.

Dr. Jastreboff is a neuroscientist with a Ph.D. He has developed a "cure." He made a medical breakthrough that humankind has been searching for. He deserves a Nobel Prize. Why should he have one? Because he will save Carol's life! And many other lives, too! Isn't that enough of a reason? She sure thinks so. She hopes others will, too!

Hyperacusis does not feel real. It is a phenomenon of the auditory system. It is a torture, just like tinnitus. Hyperacusis makes living unreal. Carol is in the same body, but her auditory system has gained power that goes much further than one step beyond what nature intended. She is a transformation that can no longer live in the universe. Hyperacusis will force her to leave. It maims and it kills. But it can be stopped if it's understood.

Carol thinks hyperacusis has already finished her off. She feels dead. But wait! She's wrong! If she pricks her finger, it still bleeds. If she pinches her arm, it will still hurt. She is alive! And while there's life, there's hope. She knows that, too!

Carol must view life differently in order to live. It has to be a game of sorts. She is required to draw cards. She will move markers on a board. If she can make it to home plate, she will be safe. "I like happy endings," Dr. Jastreboff tells her.

The game becomes her treatment. The prize for winning is her life. It is a dangerous board she is on. It's narrow, with a deep drop below. She cannot fall. She must proceed with caution. She has to go around all the curves. Is there a chance she can win?

She hears Dr. Jastreboff's words playing and repeating in her head like her tinnitus: "Yes, it works. You can recover. You can have your life back. Yes, you can have a perfectly normal life again."

A sweet voice answers her sobbing. "My father isn't home now. He'll be back later. I'll tell him you called."

Carol needs to ask the sweet voice, "Do the generators really work?"

She responds quickly. "Yes."

Carol questions desperately, "Will I really get well?"

The young girl replies again without hesitation: "Yes!"

"Will you promise to give your dad my message?"

"Yes, I'll tell my father to call you just as soon as he gets home."

Carol asks what her name is. The daughter sounds nice. Carol is grateful to have been reassured. Ania, Dr. Jastreboff's daughter, has unknowingly just helped her to survive on this warm summer day.

At night, the onslaught of the phone ringing with the force of a symphony removes any doubts Carol may have had about the East Coast doctor. She cries out to Dr. Jastreboff, "You have to save my life! I need your help!" His voice is her help.

People fly in from all over the world to see Dr. Jastreboff. Some wait two and a half years. Meanwhile, Dr. Jastreboff gives Carol so much of his time and help. She is not even officially his patient yet. How can she be? Dr. Jastreboff has never even tested her on his equipment. He's helping her through long distance communications. *Thank God for Alexander Graham Bell!*

"I can't do it! I can't go on!"

"Yes, you can!" Dr. Margaret Jastreboff, Dr. Jastreboff's wife, says, as she answers the phone. She has a doctorate and works with her husband helping patients, too. She acquaints herself with Carol. She talks calmly and matter-of-factly also. It's apparent that she, like her husband, is very sure that Carol will be well in the future.

"We have to pay him. Aren't you ashamed?" Fred says. "He's spending hours with you on the phone and at his own expense."

Carol sends a fax of thanks. She asks that Dr. Jastreboff bill them. He completely ignores this fax. This is to be his only failed response.

Carol's panic turns to sheer terror! She's in the bottom of a coffin, sealed in. She doesn't feel alive, but a part of her mind knows she is. She is living a nightmare. The frightening screen movies are made up. Her movie plays as life with an out-of-body plot. She's convinced that her only escape is her exit in this Game of Living. She views it as a final act of mercy for herself.

Dr. Jastreboff offers her a different door to go through. Only she's finding his rules too difficult to handle. The walk to reach the door is too far away.

She has a large holder of cellophane tape. She lives in a small room referred to as "the den." The den is on the far side of the house. It's furnished with a bed, piano, a desk, and a chair. She tapes Dr. Jastreboff's papers to the wall over her bed, the latest furniture added to this room. She makes a shrine to keep herself alive.

Carol reads what her son has written as she tapes it on the wall: "Mom, try to be patient. The habituation treatment will work. The instruments will refocus your brain on different sounds if you wear them long enough and diligently. I hope you have a speedy recovery. Love, David." She touches his words like they have touched her heart.

"I know every movement I make is amplified!" Carol cries out to Fred. "It's just hideously worse now!"

"For God's sake, you have the doctor and the treatment. Why can't you get by now?" Fred asks angrily. "Here, wear these—you should be able to do whatever you want. Have a nice day." He kisses her good-bye on the cheek.

She watches Fred walk so easily out the door, out into sound, out into the world. He expects her to do the same, wearing earmuffs. She looks down at the large *Thunder 29 Muffs*. They're no strangers to her. They block out a lot of the environmental noise. Nothing is enough, though, to relieve her agony.

Carol knows Dr. Jastreboff has an exceptionally high IQ. She figures that he is a genius. If she were to tell him this, she knows he would deny it. He seems so humble about all the unbelievable qualities she recognizes he possesses. He has no ego whatsoever. She can tell, even though she is very sick. Fred has taught her the meaning of that word.

Carol knows that Dr. Jastreboff's knowledge on the auditory system and these conditions is greater than anyone else's in the world. She deduces all this from the fact that he is familiar with every complexity that she has.

"No, you will not lose any benefit from the generators if you wear the earmuffs," Dr. Jastreboff says, reassuringly.

Carol doesn't have the faintest idea that special auditory testing by Dr. Jastreboff is essential for him to determine how to best help her. He's been treating her long distance from clear across the United States. She knows that even though he can only hear her cries of suffering and death, he really wants to help her!

Carol experiments with the earmuffs.

"Sure. I'd love to take a drive to Sausalito with you, Mom. Are you sure that you can?" David wants to know.

"No, but I want to try."

"I'm doing great, aren't I?" she asks, as she shakes with fear. Carol wants to show her son that she can still drive, despite her traumatized state. She struggles to ignore the thunderous noise of each passing car. She is driving, but she feels like it's through a tunnel. The tunnel roars as if a volcano has erupted and the lava is flowing down.

The sky is clear, and the sun shines brightly. The Richmond-San Rafael Bridge seems so long today on the way to the beautiful city of Sausalito. Her illness has been lengthy. She hopes she'll make it to the other side.

Carol and David walk from the car in Sausalito. She wears the muffs over her generators to block out the street noises. She feels as if she were in Spain. The people surrounding them are screaming, "The bulls are coming. Run or be killed!" Carol starts to scream. She collapses on the sidewalk, crying out in horror. Her son bends down and takes her hand.

David's eyes are tearful. "Let's go inside, off the street, into this little store."

"Okay." She is fearful and apprehensive. She continues to cry. The store is filled with music and people. The people increase the sound level. Carol has lost her physical existence in the world. Now she hears trains coming. They resound in unison. Their lyrics are easy to define. "Get off the tracks!"

Carol runs out of the store, screaming hysterically. "I can't do it! I can't stay here! I can't even walk on the street! Dear God, I can't live anymore. I don't want to! I'm sorry, David!"

She watches David as he drives her home.

Chapter 20

Carol immediately cries out to Dr. Jastreboff through another fax. He understands her pain. "Be patient and keep going with the generators."

She is too traumatized to walk around. She lies in bed all day. She swallows large quantities of tranquilizers and cries.

Dr. Jastreboff writes in his fax, "You can get a *Noisebuster* at Radio Shack." She already has this equipment. Fred had mailed it to her in Texas. She also tried it in the mental ward, not knowing why. Now she tries wearing it on top of the generators.

Carol stands next to her new refrigerator. She has the *Noisebuster* over her generators. She switches to the earmuffs. "Oh, my gosh! Neither one takes down the level," she tells Fred. The cycling refrigerator sounds like the thunder of a tornado swirling toward their home.

"Why don't you see what happens when you open the door?" Fred suggests. She cautiously opens it a crack.

"No! No!" she screams. Her body slumps to the floor in defeat and shock. She is totally debilitated from sound. She contemplates what to do.

She hops up and turns off the light switch. Next she unplugs the refrigerator, toaster, microwave, mixer, and juicer—anything with a cord attached—so they can't growl at her. She removes the battery from the kitchen clock on the wall so the second hand will stop its noisy ticking. She eyes the cuckoo clock suspiciously, searching for any signs of "life." If it moves, she'll have to slay it!

It is Carol who is the avenger, removing the obstacles in her path. She runs from room to room like the lunatic that everyone thinks she has become. She breathes fast. She feels dizzy. She tries to calm down. She swallows some more tranquilizers, hoping they'll work quickly. She throws herself down on her bed. The pillow feels comforting. Carol lies sobbing. Finally, she feels drowsy.

She finds herself in another place. *Drums are beating and booming. Cannibals have her tied to a tree. The woods echo with the chirping of crickets. Waves crash onto the beach. Birds squawk through thundershowers. Water gurgles to the beat of the drums. The forest is dark. The night speaks out. Suddenly, she sees a light in the distance. It's a ship in the stormy ocean, far away. The flames from the fire grow taller and hotter. They sizzle and hiss. They come for her, closer and closer. All at once, she sits up and opens her eyes. Her deafening scream has pierced the house.*

"It's only a dream, Carol," Fred says as he runs in. "For God's sake!"

"It wasn't, Fred. It's my tinnitus."

He puts his arms around her to comfort her. She lays her head on his shoulder. *What's going to become of me?*

"**W**ho would want to keep living with your condition?" Celia says. Tears wet Carol's face as she hugs her friend.

"I have to try harder, Celia. I found the doctor I've been searching for these past two years. His wife and even his daughter are so caring and helpful. I have to make it! It's not just for me anymore. It's gone way beyond that. I have to show all those doctors. They hurt me, Celia, with their wrong treatments. They're still doing the same thing to many others, even when there's a Dr. Jastreboff. I don't have to listen to all these horrible noises forever. I want Dr. Jastreboff to know that I'm worth saving! He could even like me, if the 'other me' comes back. I know he will!"

She is serious. Celia starts to laugh. Carol realizes how she sounds. "At least I made you laugh. I know it's hard for you to be around me. How come you're so sympathetic the way I act?"

"Carol, for years I used to watch you through my living room window."

"You did? Why?"

"Every day at 7:00 a.m., there you were. Either you walked Peanut on the sidewalk in front of my house, or you pedaled by on your bike. You wore a black sweatshirt with a hood. You had Peanut in the bike basket. You were the topic of the morning, especially when my granddaughter Erica was young and staying here. She would say, 'There goes the wicked witch on her broomstick!'"

"She did? I never met her. How did she know I was a wicked witch?" Carol giggles.

Celia laughs loudly. "She didn't! She just used that as a figure of speech. She thought your black sweatshirt was a cape. You seemed to fly through the air because you were riding so fast. The bicycle to her was your broom. I figured anyone who is out on the street at the crack of dawn must be pretty healthy. When I ran into you in your present condition, I said to Lee, 'Something awful must be wrong with Carol. I'm going to help her in any way I can.' I just wish there was something more I could do. I feel so helpless most of the time."

Carol doesn't know how to respond. She can no longer express much joy and happiness. She starts to cry as she puts her arms around her friend. "Just your being here is enough."

Celia is the only friend in her town who truly believes her. Carol needs her. Celia is dear to her. Celia is hanging in with her. Carol is so afraid. She needs Dr. Jastreboff to not give up on her. She needs him to hang in with her, too, just like Celia is doing. Without Dr. Jastreboff, she won't make it. She is sure of it.

"Please try not to cry," Dr. Jastreboff says.

I knew he'd say that, but I just can't seem to stop.

"I don't know what to do, Dr. Jastreboff. When I walk, the noise coming out of my ears copies my movements. Every motion resounds a thousand times as loud as before. When I chew or brush my teeth . . . even when I'm having sex with Fred." *Oh, why did I say that?*

"If the tinnitus beats back and forth, when I come in contact with straight-sounding noises, they don't sound right. They jump up and down and copy exactly what's coming out of my ears, only magnified!

"I'm trying to turn on outside sounds like you told me to do. I put the television on so low I can barely hear it, but the static sounds so loud that it's impossible to concentrate on a program. The stupid static bounces back and forth instead of sounding steady like it's supposed to.

"The high-pitched tone of my tinnitus is just like that test they do for an 'alert' warning on TV. And when I touch my ears, I get loud pinging noises that sound like a doctor's tuning fork. When I eat, I hear the echo of my chewing. My ears pop all the time just like when I'm up in high altitudes. They feel so painful, it's like someone's cutting into them with a knife.

"None of those awful headsets work. They don't make anything quieter at all. In fact, they make my tinnitus sound louder when I wear them over the generators. Are you still there, Dr. Jastreboff?"

"Yes."

"I can't get a moment of relief. I'm going to die, aren't I?" she finally asks. Carol sobs uncontrollably into the phone. She tries to stop crying as she hears his voice and his emotions become fierce!

"No! You're not going to die!" He talks so confidently and so positively. His words are powerful to her. "I've seen worse!"

"How can you be worse than with all of this?" she screams back incredulously.

"You could be deaf and have the tinnitus," Dr. Jastreboff replies. "Keep the generator sound below the tinnitus level.

Keep the radio or television on, but not too loud, not louder than the other sounds in your house."

"How am I suppose to last? I can't eat anything. My chest is on fire! I'm taking all this stomach medicine."

"You have to eat. Your body needs food now. Do you like oatmeal?"

"Yes. I like everything."

"I eat oatmeal," Dr. Jastreboff confides.

You do?

"It's very healthy for you!"

"I know."

"Take a little water and salt. Use the regular kind of oatmeal, not the instant, and stir it into boiling water."

Should Carol stop this wonderfully kind doctor and tell him she knows how to make oatmeal? She just doesn't know how she can eat it. Instead, she listens, amazed that he's being so caring.

"You have to keep cooking it for a while. You can add a little cream or whatever you want, and you'll have so much nourishment. If you want to get well, you will!"

"I do! I do! No one can want to get well more than I do! Thank you. I love you, Dr. Jastreboff."

Carol looks up at her clanging clock. The cord sits happily plugged into its socket. She adds the three-hour difference onto the time the clock reads. Dr. Jastreboff has called her after midnight.

Carol talks to God silently, as she knows others critically suffering must do. This is her salvation.

Dr. Jastreboff understands and feels my agony. I'm one hundred percent sure. I'd bet my life on it. Funny, because my life is already bet on him. What is he counting on to keep me going? Himself? His generators? My former strength? He's so confident in his generators and his protocol, but I know that it's going to take a lot more to keep me interested in living with this kind of torture and horror.

Dr. Jastreboff never knew me before, though he did see me in the photographs. None of my girlfriends would ski in that altitude. *My friends don't bike ride or dive off boats in the middle of the ocean either. But then none of my girlfriends are fighting for their lives. And they don't have to defend their mental states.*

Telephones are a great source of sound, but they scare Carol. They cause her pain. She understands her fears now. There is no escape from sound.

Celia telephones. She calls frequently to see if Carol is holding on, if she is still alive.

She tells her about Dr. Jastreboff. "Wouldn't you love a man like that?" Carol says to Celia. "If other doctors had a fraction of the goodness and kindness he possesses, boy! would we have less suffering and misery in the world."

"I agree!" Celia chimes in.

"Celia, I need to go to Baltimore. He gives me hope that getting well and recovering are much more than a dream. He makes it sound so positive. You don't suppose the Jastreboffs would let me live in their house, so I wouldn't die?"

"That's a bit much to expect, Carol, don't you think?" Celia chuckles. "You sound so much better every time you talk to him. I told Lee you sounded great after you spoke to his wife and daughter, too. I can tell you're holding on more strongly because you stop crying sometimes, like now. Thank God you found him, not a minute too soon!"

"Yes, Celia, I'm so thankful, but he's so far away. I don't have the confidence in myself that he does. I don't know if I can stay alive long enough to see what happens with his treatment. I first have to unload the hyperacusis before the generators can even begin to touch the tinnitus. Then like his paperwork says, it can take anywhere from eleven to eighteen months to get to the point where I may not hear the tinnitus a majority of the time, or maybe not at all. I have to endure all this suffering. I don't have a choice, not if I want my life back!"

Celia is speechless.

"**D**r. Jastreboff is the only doctor in the world who knows what to do about tinnitus and hyperacusis," Carol tells Jim. "Unfortunately, the whole world doesn't know about him." *They will if I live. I swear it! Make me live, God.*

Carol will wait for God to do his work. She is angry with Jim for not believing in her wonderful doctor. *I'll be Dr. Jastreboff's proof! I'll show everyone!*

"**F**red, I have 'Gerd'!"
"What?"
"Gastroesophageal reflux disease. The small amount of food I'm trying to swallow is refluxing back up into my throat. It feels like I'm having a heart attack! It's much worse than heartburn. The gastrointestinal pamphlets that I'm reading say to reduce stress." Tears roll down her face. "How am I supposed to do that?"

Fred tries to get Carol to see his chiropractor. He succeeds. She agrees to determine whether adjustments to her vertebrae will affect her condition. She finds out that they don't. Now she is in pain from muscle soreness. She lies on ice thinking to a time ahead when her struggle to live will be over. There is now someone on the opposite coast who is thinking of her and fighting for her to win. Carol reads about him again:

> Dr. Jastreboff received a Master of Science degree in Electronic Engineering in 1969 and a Master of Science in Biophysics in 1971 from the University of Warsaw, Poland. In 1973, he received a Ph.D. in Neuroscience from the Polish Academy of Science and an Sc.D. from this same institution in 1982. He did his postdoctoral training at the University of Tokyo, Japan. His research has been focused on the auditory and vestibular systems and on pain perception. He holds Visiting Professor appointments at Yale University School of Medicine and at University College, London, U.K. and at Middlesex Hospital, London, U.K.

"Gee! He sure has good credentials, Fred." She already knows he has a good heart! Carol keeps reading. . . .

Dr. Jastreboff has two medical doctors collaborating with him: William C. Gray, MD, an Associate Professor of Surgery; and Jonathan W. P. Hazell, MD, of London.

She knows that Dr. Jastreboff has already set up his protocol in England. He's going around the world lecturing and training professionals in other countries, too! Carol dreads the thought of his being in a faraway country. Her dependency on him is growing, along with her panic.

"I'm going to call this internist in New Jersey, Fred, from the *Hyperacusis Bulletin*."

"I thought you hate all doctors because they don't know and understand about your condition."

"My feelings haven't changed. This particular medical doctor suffers from hyperacusis. He has published articles: 'My Personal Experience with Hyperacusis as a Patient and as a Physician' and 'The Eye as a Model for Understanding the Disability of Hyperacusis.' See—his name is Elliot Rosenberg, MD." Carol shows Fred the published work.

"It's making me sad to read how he has to stuff tissues into his ears so his patients won't notice. That's just in order to use the stethoscope with his horrible hyperacusis. My heart is aching. He says his life is a disaster, along with his career." Carol wipes at her always tear-filled eyes.

"Who are you?" a very low voice asks.

"I have tinnitus and hyperacusis. I live in California. I'm wearing generators to alleviate the conditions. Have you heard of Dr. Jastreboff?" Carol doesn't wait for his response. "He has the correct treatment."

"Who? I don't think so. I'm busy now trying to spend time with my children," Dr. Rosenberg replies.

Carol thinks the doctor sounds uninterested in her well-meaning call, but she persists. If there is one thing she is, it's aggressive. She is also intuitive. Dr. Rosenberg wants her to hang up, immediately. She tries one more time.

"Do you have a fax machine?"

"No. Can you please write to me?" he asks, along with an abrupt good-bye.

She stares at the phone. Her handwriting is unreadable. Her hands shake less when she types so that's how she sends all her faxes to Dr. Jastreboff. She tries to endure the loudness from the typewriter. Every chore has increased in difficulty, just as her auditory system has with the hyperacusis.

Carol is hurt by Dr. Rosenberg's abruptness. *He didn't seem to appreciate my gesture to try to help him. Maybe he isn't as sick as I am. He took offense. He's the internist, not me. Did I do something wrong? Should I mind my own business, especially with a doctor? I probably won't live through this myself, and here I am trying to help someone else.*

She tries to put Dr. Rosenberg out of her mind. She tries not to feel guilty for butting in. She doesn't know it today, but soon he's going to be in her mind for the rest of her life.

Chapter 21

"What am I going to do?" she cries as she redials Dr. Jastreboff's office number. No one answers. "Donna and he always tell me when they're going to be away." She sobs and dials his home number. She gets his answering machine.

"Hello? This is Carol. Please call me right away! It's an emergency! I can't hang on! I'm going to end my life! I need you, Dr. Jastreboff! Please call me! Help me! Please help me!"

Her hands shake as she dials his office again. Maybe someone will come back. She can't remember how many messages she is leaving and on which machines. She is crying hysterically again. She can't endure the multiple tinnitus sounds along with the magnified outside sounds. The torment is too severe. The phone, wet from her tears, shakes in her hand. She yells into it, demandingly, "Where are you, Dr. Jastreboff? Today is Thursday. How can you go on vacation when I'm dying here?"

Carol collapses, sobbing. She realizes what she has just said and how it sounded! It's too late! It's already on the machine. *Which one?* She has way overstepped her bounds. *He'll hate me! I'm going to lose him. Now I'll surely die without his help!* She doesn't know how to live and she doesn't know how to die. Now she dreads hearing back from Dr. Jastreboff. *Please make his answering machine break down! Please don't let him call me, God. I'm not strong enough to hear him say, "I won't be bothering with you anymore, Carol."*

"I told you not to call Dr. Jastreboff every other minute, didn't I? I can't believe what you say to him. He's not one of your friends. He's a very important doctor." Fred scolds her sternly.

I deserve it! He leaves for work.

Carol sits up. She realizes that the drugs have given her an hour of rest. She is confused. She has relived her horrible behavior in her sleep. She realizes that Fred is not at home. He's working in his office. He didn't say, "I told you so!" *I must have dreamed it.*

She punishes herself over and over for her screaming phone messages to the one doctor in the world she truly trusts. She waits each day for the guillotine to drop.

Friday comes and goes. Carol watches the clock. She hears its pounding noise. Each second rips through her ears, telling her how horrible a person she has become! She isn't lovable anymore. She's mean and rotten!

Saturday and Sunday go by. Her phone stays silent. It must be a sign of his anger. Monday is the same. She is out of the woods, because Dr. Jastreboff is never going to call. He will never, never want to do another thing to help her. She is an abusive, overbearing person. All the adjectives she applies to her husband when she is angry with him now really belong to herself!

"No! No!" Carol screams out as she rewinds her answering machine. "I knew it! This message proves it. He hates me!" She sinks to the floor, sobbing.

His voice sounds stern. "Hello, this is Dr. Pawel Jastreboff calling for Mr. Brook. I would like him to please call my office as soon as he receives this message. Please call me in private. It is very important that Mrs. Brook not be anywhere near the phone."

"Celia! Help me! Please! It's all over! I've lost everything! I've lost Dr. Jastreboff!"

"Come on, Carol. It can't be that bad!"

"Oh, but it is! I might as well kill myself and get it over with. I'm not human anymore, Celia. I'm this creature-feature, this zombie that has been beamed down from another planet. That's where I belong with this condition, in outer space. Nobody on earth believes this phenomenon except the doctor who now hates me. I'm already debilitated. I live like a vegetable. I thought nothing worse could happen. But it isn't true. This is worse!"

"So what are you going to do now?"

"I don't know!" she sobs to her friend. *That's why I called you.*

"If I can trust you and you'll do as I say, I'll return Dr. Jastreboff's call from home instead of from here in my office,where he thought his message had connected," Fred tells Carol.

"Of course you can trust me. What kind of a thing is that to say? I'll do whatever you want me to. I promise!" she tearfully adds for confirmation.

"I don't want to make you feel worse, but I just called his secretary, Donna."

"You did what?"

Fred goes on nonchalantly. "Donna said I should call Dr. Jastreboff tomorrow morning at eight o'clock our time—will you stop that crying! I'll tell you what she said, but you have got to stop crying!"

"I'm sorry."

"I have work to get done from right now until tomorrow. I have deadlines. This is not fun and games, you know. By the time I grocery shop and run to a half dozen stores to get what you want, my whole day is gone!"

"I won't bother you. I promise. Now just tell me the rest of what Donna said."

"Okay. She said that Dr. Jastreboff doesn't want you to know what we discuss."

"Oh, my God!"

"I'm not to tell you. Those are his specific instructions."

"Oh, no! My God! I knew it!"

"I'm going to tell you what he discusses with me, only because you'll feel worse than you do by not knowing. Besides I know you won't stop hounding me until I do. I just can't go through anything more. I have to get ready for tax season."

"Thank you, thank you! I appreciate everything that you're doing, really!"

"I know you do."

T he next morning. . . .

"It's eight o'clock, Fred."

"Already? Okay. I'm up. Go down the hall now. I'm going to call from the bedroom phone. I want you to keep your door closed and not come out. When I finish talking, I'll come in and tell you everything that Dr. Jastreboff said."

"Everything? You promise?"

"Yes, everything."

"Okay."

Carol watches Fred close the bedroom door. Her upcoming doom is near! *I'm not ten years old. I can't just stay in my room. I have rights!* She tiptoes down the hallway and puts her head against the door. She still has perfect hearing—in fact, too perfect. She has hyperacusis. *Why can't I hear anything?* Fred is not talking. *What is Dr. Jastreboff telling him?*

Finally, she hears, "Would you please wait a second. I need to grab a pad and pencil and write that down."

More silence follows. Carol starts trembling. She is so cold and terrified of whatever is going on. But exactly what is? The whole thing seems strange! *Why isn't Fred pulverizing me like I deserve?*

"Eustachian tube?" Fred says. His voice sounds puzzled. "Thanks a million!"

She feels the tenseness ease out of her body, only to have it come back a moment later. "What about all her phone calls to you, and her constant faxing?"

There—now he's done it! Did he have to remind Dr. Jastreboff? Things seemed to be going better than I expected.

"Yes, yes, I see. Thank you. Great. Thank you. Okay, then I'll wait for your call."

Carol is dripping with sweat. She stands leaning next to the door, her head tipped to one side. She races as fast as she can back down the hallway. She closes the door, grabs a book, and sits on her bed. She looks up as Fred enters. He looks down at his pad. She appears to wait patiently.

"How bad is it?" she asks, timidly.

"It's not bad at all." She looks perplexed. She is relieved. Now she gets bolder.

"But I called and faxed him a million times!"

"Yes, well, cool it, can you? Dr. Jastreboff is very busy, and what you're doing isn't good for him. The whole university sees your faxes coming in. They know that you're not even his patient! You don't want to cause him any trouble, do you? He's being extraordinarily kind to you."

"I know! I know! I won't do it anymore, I promise!" *Am I lying?* She wonders why this doesn't seem to be the subject that was discussed.

"Dr. Jastreboff wants to have you tested for"—Fred glances down at his notepad—"'Patulous Eustachian Tube Syndrome.' You describe the outside sounds as slurred, so he thinks there's a chance you may have this condition."

"Yea!" She screams with joy and jumps up and down on her bed. "I knew I had something, something that can be immediately fixed that will stop all this noise!"

Before she can utter anything more than her screams of joy, Fred bluntly says, "Your reactions are exactly why Dr. Jastreboff does not want you to know what we've talked about. He definitely doesn't want to raise your hopes or have you count on this as your cure. His generators will eventually alleviate your whole condition over a period of time. Anyway, you'll have to be tested for this. He's going to try to set it up locally and will let us know when and where."

"But I can't live through the severity of this with just the generators."

"I'm sure this is why he's trying his best to think of anything that might apply to what you've told him. He only wants to check this out just in case you do have it. I don't need to remind you that he is guessing from 3,000 miles away and without his own test results of your auditory system. He'll fax a description of the condition, along with the procedure for correcting it. From what he explained, it's a surgical thing whereby an instrument goes down through your nose. It applies pressure to the Eustachian tube, and it's done under an anesthetic."

"God! Who's going to do the surgery?"

"See, in just two minutes, you've already convinced yourself, without the test, that you're on your way to an operating table. This is exactly why Dr. Jastreboff doesn't want you to know. He needs time to locate a doctor with whom he can discuss you getting the test."

"Locate a doctor, Fred? Oh, my gosh! You mean not all ear surgeons know how to test for this condition?"

"No, they don't! He knows only a couple of doctors in the United States with any correct knowledge about the condition."

Carol says angrily to Fred, "Why should I expect the ear specialists to know what this Eustachian tube thing is anyway? Most of them don't even know what hyperacusis is!" *They better hope I die!* She feels vengeful. She wants justice.

"It's hard to discuss hyperacusis because the condition is just not understood and believed!" Dr. Margaret Jastreboff confirms. Carol listens in horror! "I'll have Pawel call you as soon as he returns."

Carol loves Dr. Jastreboff's wife, too. She's so thankful for her help now.

"I'm sorry for everything I say that isn't nice, Dr. Jastreboff. Why are you doing all this for me?" She tries really hard not to cry. She tries to put on her best behavior attitude.

"I can never relieve my mind of your suffering. It's just there—with me—all the time," Dr. Jastreboff responds.

Carol will never forget the words he has just spoken. Her heart overflows with gratitude and appreciation. She is overwhelmed by his concern.

"I've studied your faxed information, and I know I have this condition. I have to! I have all the symptoms."

"Go into your bathroom and swallow some water. Try to breathe through your nose while you are swallowing. Then come back to the phone and tell me if your tinnitus sounds different."

"You'll wait right there? You won't go away?"

"Yes, I'll be right here, waiting."

She runs to the bathroom sink. The heat is on in her house. The sound is deafening. She looks up at the vents. They represent a roaring monster. The creature is spewing venom. There is no escape. There is no safe place where sound cannot reach. Carol returns to the phone, shaking. "I can't tell anything!"

"All right. It's okay. We'll have to wait for the test results then."

A few days later, Carol is telling Dr. Jastreboff, "I called a local ear surgeon. He's supposed to be very skilled. He actually doesn't know anything about the Patulous Eustachian Tube Syndrome."

"I'm not surprised," Dr. Jastreboff responds.

It is very difficult for her to understand that she has something doctors don't know anything about. "Dr. Jastreboff, what if you told this same ear doctor that you're hearing everything a thousand times too loud? Then they would want to give you a bed just like me in the mental ward!" she says seriously to her doctor back East. She sadly knows that they would, too.

Dr. Jastreboff laughs! Carol enjoys hearing him laugh. She has just learned something about him. He has a good sense of humor. *I made a joke without realizing it.*

"I can't hold on. Please help me! It's not human!"

"Yes, of course it's human!" Dr. Jastreboff replies.

"No, it isn't!" she uncontrollably yells, sobbing her heart out. "How can you say that?" she asks the doctor from whom she so badly needs help. His answer reassures her: "It's human, because you're human!"

Chapter 22

Carol is deliberately outside. It is late, and it is dark. She is on her bicycle. She pedals fast. Her torture is beyond human limits. She no longer wants to endure it. She removes the headset. She needs to absolve herself from what she's about to do.

She crosses under the overpass as the **BART** train whizzes by. It produces a deafening, slurred roar. She is no longer afraid. She is no longer responsible. She moves onto the road. Her bike has no lights. She wears her black "witch's" sweatshirt and black jeans. *This is my only way out. Fred will never stop criticizing my behavior. He'll never understand the torture I'm forced to bear. He'll tell Dr. Jastreboff how well he ignores and handles his own problem. Fred has a much lower level condition than mine. Nobody will ever believe me in this town. It's time to die. I need to!*

She is crying hard. Tears block her vision. *They'll think it's an accident. Is this so wrong? Dr. Jastreboff will know. He is so far away from me. I am so cold and scared.* She hears the cars coming behind her—long before they approach.

She edges out to the center of the highway. *Dear God, let it be quick. Don't let the car injure me without killing me.*

Carol hears honking. A voice yells, "Are you crazy? Get out of the way, you nut!" She swerves back toward the curb, obeying the irate driver who fails to strike her. She sits on the curb. Her bike lies across the sidewalk. The area is deserted.

She cries hysterically. She looks up at the darkened sky. *Where are you, God? Why won't You help me?* She wipes her eyes and picks up her bike. She doesn't think it now, but God just has. She slowly pedals home, on the sidewalk, wearing her headset.

Carol tries to absorb what Dr. Jastreboff is saying.

"I want three descriptions from you," he explains. "First, describe all your sounds as they progressed, along with the treatments tried, up to the sound generators. Make separate sections. Second, tell me about your sports' accidents and symptoms. And third, make me a list of all the drugs you took—everything. Then fax it to me. I'm getting on the plane Monday for London. I want to read it during the flight. I'll try to get you an early appointment, but I can't promise a date. If I were doing the surgery, I would test you immediately!"

Dr. Jastreboff is going to try to see if the doctor in Europe will help Carol. She already believes that no other doctor anywhere will ever be as compassionate as Dr. Jastreboff is.

"How many pages can I do?"

"About eighteen is fine."

"What if it's a lot more?"

"That's okay, too."

"But your whole office is going to be covered with my faxes."

"Don't worry about that."

She clings to the phone like she clings to his every word.

"You can't use a typewriter for all that work. I'll show you how to use the computer," Fred tells her.

"I can't! The typewriter sounds like a plane engine. The computer will be like a 747—worse, probably like the Concorde," Carol tries to explain to Fred. She works day and night with her documentation. Fred works day and night to help her on the computer. And Dr. Jastreboff works day and night trying to save lives. Now he is working to save hers.

She sits at the keyboard, crying. She wears her headset over the generators.

She keys in the title "Sports/Accidents/Symptoms." *Why sports and accidents?* She types fast, entering everything she remembers. She stops midstream and stares at what she has typed. She reads past the part about her ski mishaps to her bicycle accident. Carol has detailed how she and Fred were racing their bikes on a newly opened path. Fred managed to make it across the railroad tracks, but his warning scream back to her was too late. Carol's front tire got wedged between the tracks and she was flipped over the bike.

Carol had been lucky. She had landed on and had hurt only her right knee. She hadn't been able to walk for a while, but she was eventually fine, or so she thought.

Then so many years later, in Puerto Vallarta with Fernando, the undertow in water only a foot deep caught her off balance. She landed on her fanny. Fernando laughed. She heard a snap and could no longer walk on her right leg.

Carol had no idea what happened. She had completely forgotten about her past bike incident. Even if she hadn't, the thought that her accident could bounce back over a decade later would have been ridiculous.

She describes the miraculous cortisone shot in her knee that allowed her to instantly walk again. She was able to get an injection in Puerto Vallarta which is usually only given to professional athletes in the United States.

She has done a good job listing her many accidents in chronological order. In fact, so good that she suddenly understands everything that has taken so long to discover. "Oh, no, no, no!" She lays her head on the computer and weeps for the life she has lost. She has just made a startling discovery!

After all I have put myself through, I read my own writing and suddenly everything is magically clear? This can't be! Now she knows what has caused her condition. She's in a trance!

She puts her fifty pages of documentation through the fax machine like a robot. She is bewildered. She is walking in a fog.

Carol has to meet this genius doctor back East. She has to live, if only to meet him.

Dr. Jastreboff knows. That's why he asked for all this work from me when I am so sick—wait! I have to stop my fax machine!

Carol becomes overly concerned for Dr. Jastreboff's well-being. She wants him to stay put, not take any risks. *Why am I feeling like a protective mother?* She needs him to save her life!

All of this fax paper is going to billow out of his fax machine into his hallway. When he walks toward his office, he won't look down. He'll slip and break his neck. He'll be in a cast and miss his plane. Her imagination construes the occurrence of various mishaps, all due to the slippery fax paper.

Get a grip! Nothing is going to happen to him. He is too important to the world. God will watch over him. Stop worrying! Carol somehow thinks that from this second on, she will always worry about this doctor she has yet to meet.

She tries to regain her composure. *I need to think and remember.* She glances at the symptoms excerpt. *They were present following my accident in 1989. Oh, my God! The accident in Bermuda!* Only an empty house hears her anguish.

She is supposed to die, but she doesn't. She is in an ambulance. The siren blares. She's in shock, but alive. Her neck and head are sore. She has whiplash, but she isn't afraid.

It's happening now. Stop it! Make it come out differently. ·

"**D**on't go to Bermuda! Carol! Are you still there?"

Carol pictures Fred sitting at his desk in his office in Alameda. She looks up at Fernando grinning at her. Always the comedian. Fernando keeps shaking the stupid boat tickets in front of her. He keeps trying to tempt her.

She remembers the guilt and Fernando's words, "Are you going to talk about Fred the whole trip?" He makes a funny face to make her laugh. "Do you want to dive off now and swim back?" he asks, as she watches the Statue of Liberty grow smaller and smaller.

They have just returned from a business trip to the Paris fashion shows, followed by a strenuous work session in the garment district of New York. And now a guilt trip to Bermuda, the fun part.

She looks at the waves the boat makes. She pictures her skis going over the wake back and forth, back and forth. She wouldn't mind water-skiing to shore.

"Smile, Carolina, come on. It's not that bad," Fernando continues. "We'll only be a few days. Then you can go back to Fred." He laughs at what he has just said. Fernando knows Fred, too! He snaps a picture of Carol with his camera. He hands her a plastic glass filled with champagne.

Carol remembers every detail. She even has a picture in her album. She has lots of pictures of their past travels all over the world. "Oh, Fernando . . . if only you were here to know how very bad everything is for your very best friend."

She feeds the last pages to Dr. Jastreboff into her fax machine. She remembers what her mother said. "You and Fernando act like six-year-olds. Have fun, but be careful!" She closes her eyes, reliving moments.

"Can you get the taxi?" her fashion designer friend asks in Bermuda. But the taxi doesn't pull up in the driveway. Instead, the driver waits on the deserted road across the way.

"You'll recover! You'll be well! You'll have a normal life back. Then I'd like you to go in front of the cameras," Dr. Jastreboff says on the phone from Baltimore, Maryland.

"You can be a spokesperson if you want," Dr. Margaret Jastreboff, his wife, adds.

"Help me!" Carol screams in vain. "God help me!" she shrieks, six years after her crash, standing at her fax machine. "Transmission okay," the machine says, as her thoughts drift back . . . back to Bermuda.

"The taxicab is here," the doorman walks over to tell Fernando and Carol. They sit in a nightclub sipping drinks. Fernando doesn't want to watch another flame dancer perform. He wants to leave. "Let's go downtown to a disco. Won't that be fun?"

"Wait up, Fernando," Carol yells, as she tries to button her latest knitting project.

"Get in," Fernando screams from the taxi into the night.

"Just a minute. I need the headlights of the cab to see how to get my sweater closed. I knit the buttonholes really lopsided." Carol makes a mental note to knit better in the future.

Fernando doesn't hear her mumble what she's doing in front of the cab in the middle of the night. She finally plops down next to her friend. He has deliberately chosen the back row of the large taxi so they can talk without the driver listening in.

"What took you so long?"

Carol starts to answer. She hears a crash. She feels the impact. She can't speak. Fernando's scream says it for her: "We're going to die!"

The cab is off the ground. It has wings! It's flying through the air. There's a steep drop on the left. It's a dark night. The cab will roll down the embankment and explode. Carol is helpless. She's too young to die. She waits for the flames. She wants to live!

"We landed upright," Fernando says to the doctor in the hospital emergency room.

"You both are very, very lucky!" The doctor shines his light into their eyes. "Don't hesitate to call me if you have any problems."

"Can you imagine that?" Fernando is angry. Carol and Fernando look for a pay phone to call another cab. "Not only will no one give us a ride back to the ship, they actually want us to pay for our hospital visit, too!" he says, disgusted.

Carol looks at Fernando. They both start to laugh. Soon they are hysterically laughing all the way to the ship—in another taxicab.

"Don't think of suing. You're not in 'your' United States." Carol is in the local Bermuda police station the next morning. She's furious at the policeman's audacity when she is the victim.

"*We never sue anyone so you have nothing to worry about,*" she answers.

"*I have the driver of the truck in the drunk tank, if that makes you feel any better.*"

He was drunk? A truck hit us? "*It doesn't,*" she says to the policeman as she rubs her sore head. Carol leaves the station wondering how she will tell Fred.

Chapter 23

Carol and Fred are in Los Angeles. Carol wears a headset. She cries all the time now. The noises from the plane, the street, and the world blast deafening sound through her ears. Wearing the headset barely gets her by. It magnifies the tinnitus. She is in excruciating pain. Her constant crying out is making Fred miserable, too. He still doesn't understand the extent of her suffering. Only Dr. Jastreboff does. Her doctor's words and voice replay in her head. She has every word that he has said to her memorized. She is his patient. He is responsible for her destiny.

"I want you to see two different specialists in Los Angeles," Dr. Jastreboff has instructed. "Both doctors are capable of doing the Eustachian tube testing. It's always good to have two opinions."

"Your results came out negative." So much for the first opinion.

"No, no! This can't be right! Please do the test again! You have to! I can't even walk in front of a car!"

"Then walk behind it," the humorous doctor replies.

Carol looks at this well-known ear surgeon with daggers. She's suffering and he's making jokes. People have told her that a former President of the United States went to him in the past. Fred tries to stifle a laugh!

"I want you to do the test again," she requests. He does.

"It's the same. Negative!"

Carol knows everyone ill wants to test negative. She doesn't.

"I really can't determine what's wrong with you unless you take my battery of tests," this distinguished doctor with the keen sense of humor states. "See my secretary at the front desk."

"The tests run around three thousand dollars," the office worker informs Fred, who no longer looks in a joking mood. The secretary looks at Carol as she speaks to Fred. "Your wife has to be off all drugs for twenty-four hours before she takes our tests. Do you want to set up an appointment?"

Carol knows she cannot endure one hour without a drug in her system, let alone twenty-four hours. She shudders at the thought. Besides, they have no travel plans for a stopover in this large, noise-filled city.

"May I please use your phone?" she asks politely, trying her best not to break down. The employee nods "yes" and motions her behind the counter.

"The test came out negative! I don't want to live anymore! It's completely impossible for me," she cries from the Los Angeles medical office to Dr. Jastreboff in his home in Baltimore.

"I want you to go over to the other doctor now while you're in Los Angeles. Call me and let me know what he says."

Carol has to go on living. Dr. Jastreboff wants her to call him again. "Can I call you at your home?" she hesitantly asks. She needs to test the waters. She needs to be sure he really wants her to stay alive.

"Yes."

"Thank you. I will." She wipes away the tears that have dripped down onto the sweater she made when she was a "normal" person.

"I'm sorry, but your test came out negative," the second doctor advises. *He has just signed my death warrant!* She can't hold on. She wants to live, but it's not possible. Her strength and will are gone! *I was so sure this was the answer!*

Carol screams hysterically in uncontrollable anguish from the hotel room in Los Angeles. "I need you, Dr. Jastreboff! I need to see you! Can I come to Baltimore? Will you give me the Patulous Eustachian test again? I know you have other patients on waiting lists, but I just can't live any longer this way!"

"Yes. I'll see you and I'll test you. No stone will be left unturned," he promises her. She believes him. He is like a god to her.

Who would believe that ears can torture and kill?

Each second that clangs like a cymbal crawls like a snail. Carol watches the clock, swallows her drugs, and cries out in anguish.

The shower continues to echo like a thousand slurred bumblebees. She hangs onto the door, afraid that she'll pass out. She hears blasting, buzzing roars as if masses of voices are joined in chanting.

Carol cries out to Dr. Jastreboff by fax and phone, day and night. He answers her calls immediately. He leaves everything to come to her aid. He wills her to be strong. He wills her to live on. She inscribes his words into her heart. She pastes his written responses all over the house she can no longer function normally in.

"I can't take a shower!" she yells into the phone.

"Try taking a bath," Dr. Jastreboff answers.

Her bathrooms are torture chambers. She drugs herself to be able to use them. She drugs herself to continue to exist and to suffer more.

Fred casually says, "The roofers are here. They'll be working on our house today."

"Oh, no!"

Carol has boxes of pills that she must take. She is very thin and very cold. She shakes and she cries. She wants to run, but where? And to whom?

She races over to Celia's. The world is alive. Only she is dead. She gasps for breath outside. One bird's tweeting resounds like that of thousands. She cannot see them. She can only hear their voices. The trees swaying in the breeze resemble hundreds of water hoses putting out a disastrous fire. The cars are not airplanes, but to her they all have jet engines.

What's that? A dog crosses her path. If he barks, he'll sound like a prehistoric beast, a dinosaur—some creature from another time and place.

She is the visitor here, not the innocent animal. She has been beamed down into a world where she can no longer exist. She wants to leave immediately, but Dr. Jastreboff wills her to wait and be patient. He has made an appointment for her in his clinic. He wants to save her life! She hopes she might be the biggest challenge he will ever have, because if he can save her, he will be able to save anyone with these afflictions. If he can bring her to a full recovery, he can bring anyone else to a full recovery.

A lion is rubbing against my face. "It's only a cat," she says, relieved. She looks at the tiny animal. "Cats don't bark." She pets Celia's cat. She tries to sleep on Celia's couch.

Celia's grandfather clock is Carol's next assailant. It jangles her frayed nerves. She can't tolerate anything in her friend's living room. The outside street and her home a block away wait for her like the open mouth of the shark in *Jaws*. If she goes out the front door, the street will get her. If she makes it to her house, the roofers will scrape up the remains of her mental health.

No one is strong enough to save her, not even Dr. Jastreboff. It's too long a struggle. It's too hard a fight.

"William Shatner is my patient now," Dr. Jastreboff says to her on the phone.

"I saw his picture on the American Tinnitus Association's quarterly journal. He looks so handsome." She starts to cry. "I need another patient of yours, Dr. Jastreboff. I need someone to talk to. I'm so alone. I'm not going to last until my plane flight to Baltimore." Carol's cries increase.

"I'll help you. Please don't cry," Dr. Jastreboff says sadly. He hesitates. She waits for him to respond. "All my other patients have only bits and pieces of what you have. Yours is a very complex case. You have not only what my other patients have but other things as well, things that I have only read and studied about."

"Oh, my God!" The extent of what Dr. Jastreboff says is incredible!

"I found an ear, nose, and throat surgeon at the Medical Research Center in Oregon. He sounds nice and kind," Carol tells Fred.

"What did you do that for? You have only a few weeks until our trip to see Dr. Jastreboff in Baltimore. Why in heaven's name did you call another doctor?" Fred sounds very annoyed. This time, he has a good reason.

"I can't swallow, Fred. I want someone connected with tinnitus to see why my chest won't heal!"

"You know they believe in masking and using Xanax there, don't you?"

"Of course I do. I'll never stop following Dr. Jastreboff's protocol. I'm just afraid I'll die in the meantime if I can't eat. What if my digestive tract is permanently damaged?"

Fred agrees to take Carol to the ENT doctor in Oregon. He makes the travel arrangements for their trip.

Carol sits at the airport wearing her earmuffs over the generators. She is having second thoughts. "We don't have to go." She shudders from the volume of accumulative noise the airport is making right through the heavy muffs.

"Oh, yes we do! I want you to know that after we go to Oregon, there isn't going to be anyplace left in the world where any doctor will even remotely be able to understand what you have!" Fred announces this so loudly that Carol thinks everybody in the whole airport understands.

The scenery that Oregon is famous for looks beautiful. She would give anything to be able to walk on the street, look in the stores, and eat in the restaurants.

"You don't expect me to stay in the office while that instrument goes down your nose and throat, do you?"

"No." Carol watches Fred take a seat outside the doctor's room. She is thankful and lucky he is exceptionally magnanimous with the money he spends on his sick wife. At the moment, though, she feels unlucky as the surgical tool turns about in her esophagus.

"It looks inflamed," the doctor says. "But that's all I can see. You should continue taking Prevacid or Prilosec. I'll talk more to you later, after your sound tests."

"I'm definitely not switching from Dr. Jastreboff's methods," Carol defiantly states. She wears Dr. Jastreboff's generators, and she is walking with the testing doctor toward the sound room.

"So you're seeing Dr. Jastreboff, is that it?"

"Yes!" She can tell his angry reaction by his tone of voice when he emphasized her doctor's name. Her presence with her treatment protocol makes him annoyed, but she doesn't care. In fact, she is enjoying herself as much as it is possible in her condition. *This is going to be interesting.* She cares only how Dr. Jastreboff feels about her.

"Your tinnitus high-pitched tone is bad!" the Oregon sound testing doctor announces.

"I know," she answers in agreement. *So tell me something I don't know.* She listens patiently to him explain the merits of masking to cover up tinnitus. *Now it's my turn.*

"How can you cover up the multiple changing tones that I have?" She challenges him on purpose. She already knows the answer. It's impossible! She is deliberately going out of her way to be unpleasant, like so many doctors have been to her. She feels vindictive. *Every doctor practicing in this field is injuring patients like me. This has to stop. I will see that it does! Only first—one small detail—I have to live to recover!*

"We can't," he answers honestly. "But we can match and cover up one tone. We can cover up your hissing tone with the noise our maskers make. After you leave it turned up over your own tone, when you remove the masker, you'll have some residual habituation. In other words, we can wipe out your own tone for a few minutes at a time, to give you some relief."

He thinks this is amazing. This is completely useless in her case! Since Carol has hyperacusis, she can't run his tone higher than her tinnitus, because she can't tolerate the sound. So she couldn't cover up even one tinnitus tone if she wanted to. Even though they're trying to help her, she feels like she's in enemy territory.

Should she explain her hyperacusis to this doctor? Then she could explain what Dr. Jastreboff's methods do. Carol better not even consider it. She's not a doctor. She'd probably end up fighting. The police would come. Before the police, Fred would be in here. That's worse.

She smiles, thinking of what Fred would say. "Carol, how could you? That's the last straw. I'm leaving you." She immediately stops conjuring little scenarios. She cringes at the thought of being alone with tinnitus and hyperacusis.

The kind ear surgeon with the surgical instrument says, "I really don't know anything at all about hyperacusis. I think you should stick with Dr. Jastreboff."

Carol is surprised at his admission of lack of knowledge in this area. She has the utmost respect now for this doctor. She feels his compassion and sympathy. He sounds shocked and horrified by the extent of her condition. He looks at her quite sadly. *He thinks I'm not going to live. I'll pray that he's wrong.*

She likes him a lot. He has been truthful. She gives him a tearful hug. She thanks him for examining her chest. "I do plan to stick with Dr. Jastreboff forever! I sure hope he can stand me!" The kind doctor laughs. She hopes that one day she'll laugh at everything, too.

Upon leaving the Oregon Research Center, Carol and Fred meet a woman in the waiting room. *"Ask her,"* Fernando would *laugh and say. "You ask everybody everything."*

"Excuse me. Do you have tinnitus?" Carol asks the woman who looks like a grandmother.

"I most certainly do!"

"Do you have to take drugs to get by with your tinnitus?" Carol wants to know.

"Yes, dear," the woman, who looks to be in her seventies, kindly responds. It's obvious to Carol that she has no hyperacusis. She is walking around without ear protection.

Fred details some of the things that Carol has tried, which have run up their bills to nearly $100,000, in trying to find a "cure." The woman replies, "My dear, I have had this for over thirty years. Save your money. There's no way to get rid of it!"

Carol knows in her heart that the woman is wrong.

Dr. Jastreboff's treatment does alleviate tinnitus!

Carol is determined to see Dr. Jastreboff. She wants to prove the woman from Oregon wrong. Is she going to last? Each new day seems worse than the previous one. She grows weaker and weaker from trying to endure her agony.

Why aren't all the doctors in this field united and using this only known effective method to conquer these monsters? She struggles to go along with the generators. She tries to be patient. She has to stay alive to see if the generators work like she's sure they will!

Chapter 24

Carol is barely able to hang on. She slams doors shut to block out noise. She slams her mind shut at the thought of having no peaceful existence without suffering. She finds living impossible.

In one day, she leaves twenty-six hysterical messages on Dr. Jastreboff's machine when he has gone out of town. Her cries are always the same: "Please be there for me! Please don't ever leave me! Please save me!"

"It's no use, David. I tried, but I can't go on. I have to find a way to ease my misery," she again tells her only child whom she loves with all her heart. "You'll still have your father. You'll be all right."

The realization of what she has told her son pains her more than she thinks the actual act of killing herself will. David responds, "My life will be meaningless unless you are in it! Having Dad isn't enough! I want my mom, too!"

Days later, Carol shivers from the unbearable noise level on the plane to Baltimore. *I'm going to have a heart attack right here.* She wishes the plane would crash to end her suffering. She looks at the passengers. *Please forgive me, God.*

The plane stops in Denver. This is the longest flight she has been on since the onset of her condition. She looks out the window. She watches the luggage being loaded for the connecting passengers. The baggage worker wears a ski parka. Snowflakes fall on his jacket as he hoists someone's skis onto the luggage carrier. *I once skied.* She stops looking outside. Her eyes are clouded with tears. She closes them and leans back in her seat, remembering. . . .

"That's the last time I follow you, Fernando!" She stands at the top of a steep incline. She knows that she can't remove her skis or she will drown in the deep snow.

"See you at the bottom." He waves good-bye with a pole.

"You better hide if you know what's good for you!" she yells back.

Fernando doesn't hear. He is flying around moguls. She looks down at the angle of the slope, quivering.

"I can't do this." This is a double black diamond run—the most difficult—beyond her capabilities.

"Do you want a hand?" She looks up into the face of someone who appears to be the age of her son.

"I most certainly do! Thank you!"

"Stay right behind me. I'll take the easy way," the advanced skier says. He leads her safely to the bottom. She is no longer afraid. She is out of danger.

Now Carol is no longer on the slopes, yet she is still in danger. There is no easy way down the mountain with tinnitus and hyperacusis. She has been fighting too hard and too long. She is exhausted.

Carol and Fred enter Baltimore International. She removes the headset. She's embarrassed wearing it.

"I have to check on our return tickets now, Carol. Can you help by finding out the quickest way to the hotel?"

"I can't, Fred. I'm afraid!" She turns to stare at the escalator. It represents a giant reptile which is terrorizing her. It makes a continuous clopping noise with each rung of the ladder that advances.

"You know, the Jastreboffs don't have to make a special trip over to the hotel to meet us so late at night. Without your help, we may not make it there on time. I know meeting Dr. Jastreboff before your testing session means a lot to you. Can't you do this one little thing?"

The ticket clerk behind the counter where Fred is standing tries to be helpful. "There are phones upstairs," she announces, as she looks strangely at Carol.

She must conquer the escalator. She does. She goes upstairs, freaked out. She looks at the courtesy phones with dread. The floor appears to be deserted. Carol shakes with anxiety, even in this area that she knows is reasonably quiet. To her, it parallels the sounds at an amusement park.

"Why take a cab when you can come with me?" A stranger pops out of the blue. Carol looks up, startled. "I have a car. I'll take you wherever you want to go," he continues.

Oh, really? Can't this pickup artist tell that I'm an abnormal oddity? Can't he see that I'm critically ill? Fred keeps saying that my outer appearance hasn't changed. She is wearing form-fitting jeans and western boots. She looks attractive and normal. No one sees anything different.

"No, thank you. My husband is waiting downstairs."

"I don't mind giving both of you a ride to wherever you're going," he persists.

One person isn't enough to kill? "Thank you anyway. You're very kind," she lies. Carol runs toward the escalator, trying to forget what this mode of transportation is like. She needs to get down to the first floor to safety. She rides on the back of a talking crocodile descending into the muddy waters down below.

"Fred!" She is breathless. "There's a man upstairs that's a thief and a murderer. He's trying to get me into his car!"

"Come on, no one bothers you in a public airport."

Oh, yeah? "No! That's not true!" She's mad at Fred's lack of belief in her honesty. *Maybe I exaggerated a little!*

"It's really not safe to pick up with anyone, even here," the helpful ticket lady says to Fred.

"You're absolutely right." Fred now agrees with the employee behind the counter. The ticket agent has expressed Carol's exact sentiments. Fred acknowledges the agent. Why doesn't he believe his own suffering wife?

Carol and Fred enter the lobby of the Marriott. Carol immediately notices another escalator clomping. Then she hears something far worse.

"Oh, my gosh! They're doing reconstruction in this hotel!"

"I don't like it either. Remember, I'm sensitive to some sounds, too!" Fred thinks he has what she has. She is to be tested tomorrow, here in Baltimore. So is Fred! Carol will see what Fred has. Everyone will!

"You promise now, you won't leave me for even a minute, right?" She's afraid of the hotel. Fred doesn't respond. He's too busy inquiring about the health club and massages.

Carol scans their room for power emissions. The room is full of sounds. It is impossible and unbearable. The world threatens her existence. She has to be strong. *Everything will be invisible and meaningless in Baltimore, except Dr. Jastreboff.*

Now Carol and Fred wait in the lobby by the door. She is not wearing her headset. She is self-conscious in public. She wants to look as normal as she can in the Marriott.

While Dr. Jastreboff is walking down the snow-paved streets from the clinic to meet Carol, she is pacing back and forth like a tiger in a cage. *I'm so lucky to have this wonderful, caring doctor helping me. God bless him for his unbelievable kindness, devotion, and unselfishness. His concern for human suffering is boundless!*

"Here he is!" she yells to Fred excitedly. Fred is pacing back and forth nearby, waiting and watching, too.

Carol races over to Dr. Jastreboff. He has given her so much support long distance for the past eight months. Her tears of joy drench him as she hugs and kisses him on the cheek in gratitude.

"How can I possibly have this so bad?" she cries.

"You were in the wrong place at the wrong time," he answers sadly.

She feels better just being near Dr. Jastreboff. She feels safe and protected. She instantly feels stronger emotionally. He makes it seem a certainty that she will live and recover.

"You will test me again for the Patulous Eustachian Tube Syndrome, won't you?" She is still grabbing at straws. She has already been tested twice.

"You'll get all my tests, everything. I have allotted plenty of time to spend with both you and Mr. Brook." She is reassured for the time being. She has no more to ask. She has to wait for the test results. *Please make the Patulous test be positive. My only hope is surgery for a "quick" cure.*

"There's Margaret now," Dr. Jastreboff says.

"Can I go outside in this weather without a hat over my ears?" She doesn't know what she should or shouldn't do.

"Yes," Dr. Jastreboff responds. "The weather really isn't too cold tonight. It's very refreshing."

Carol dashes out the door leaving Fred and Dr. Jastreboff chatting. She wills herself to be brave. She hears the power sources which illuminate the Marriott. They resemble numerous engines idling. She hears the sounds of the night and the street. Her desire to meet Dr. Margaret Jastreboff overrides her fears and intense anxiety. She makes her way to the car.

"You're so beautiful," she says, as she tearfully hugs Dr. Jastreboff's wife. As she listens to her, Carol thinks, *She's not only beautiful looking; she looks so healthy.* Carol is conscious of only two things in the world: noise and health. She has lost control of them both.

She dreams of regaining her ability to use sound. She prays to someday eat whatever she wants again without pain. In the Jastreboffs' presence, it seems possible. Alone, by herself, her dreams are only a fantasy.

"I haven't been home all day. I feel badly about Tobi. He hasn't been fed his dinner," Dr. Margaret Jastreboff tells Carol.

Peanut, I miss you so! "I don't want to keep you both any longer. Oh, please go right home. Tobi must be adorable. What does he look like?"

"He is quite nice, tan, and just the right size for a cocker spaniel." Carol visualizes Tobi running up to the Jastreboffs. His floppy ears wiggle as he wags his tail excitedly.

"I wish I could meet Tobi sometime," Carol says longingly. Her broken heart aches for the beloved pet she was forced to give up.

"Hi, Randie." She tries to smile the next morning at the clinic. Carol meets Randa Blackwell, the financial director of Dr. Jastreboff's Tinnitus and Hyperacusis Center.

"Would you like some coffee?" Carol would love some, but she refuses. She can barely swallow.

"Why don't you wait here in my office until you're called. It'll be less noisy." Randie's kindness is apparent and appreciated.

The testing room is silent. Carol sits on a chair in the soundproof room. She holds onto a signaling-button apparatus attached to a cord. The volume of each generated sound will be gradually increased one level at a time. She is instructed to press the button when she feels she can no longer tolerate a particular sound.

She watches Sarah, the audiologist, behind a glassed-in partition. Sarah talks into a microphone. She works on the equipment in front of her. Carol is instructed to remove her headset and generators. She puts on the special headset which is connected to the audiology equipment.

Carol follows Sarah's instructions to the letter. She weighs over her answers. She wants her several hours of testing to give accurate results to Dr. Jastreboff.

Now Carol keeps her tear-filled eyes focused on Sarah's face. *The audiologist's expression will be a dead giveaway.* Carol sits next to the sink. She watches Sarah calculate the effects of what is happening. She keeps swallowing the required water, watching and waiting. Sarah appears nervous as she administers the Patulous Eustachian Syndrome Test. *This can save me.*

"The results are negative, aren't they, Sarah?" Carol holds her breath. She wants the truth now! Sarah looks sad.

"Yes," Sarah responds, reluctantly.

I forced it out of her without Dr. Jastreboff. I'm going to die and the audiologist understands.

Chapter 25

The sound testing is painless. Working with Sarah is easy. Only living or dying is hard. Carol is proud of herself for handling the testing.

"Good-bye, Sarah, and thanks for your patience and help." Carol gives her a hug.

"Good luck, Carol."

"May the gods be with you," Fernando would say.

"How did it go?" Fred inquires.

"Fine. Why? You're dreading the sounds in your ears, aren't you?"

"Well, it doesn't seem like it would be the most pleasant experience."

"Actually I kind of enjoyed it. It's nice and quiet in there."

"Were any of the sounds painful for you to listen to?" her husband dares to ask.

I have death-causing hyperacusis! "No! Nothing! I didn't even cry."

"Why don't you go back to the hotel and get some rest until I'm done," Fred suggests.

"No! I'm too afraid to walk back alone! I definitely won't be able to do that!" Fred looks bewildered. *Why am I not surprised?*

"Well, I guess you'll have to wait for hours in the waiting room, won't you then?"

"That's okay." She sits down.

Why would anyone be even remotely nervous about the testing? Dr. Jastreboff wants to reverse the gain in the auditory system with his generators, not increase it! He would never suggest anything to make the conditions worse. He's trying to help people, not hurt them.

Fred comes out of the testing room. Carol feels like she is a burden to him. She needs him like a baby needs its mother.

Back in their hotel room, Fred says, "I'm going down to the exercise room to take a hot tub."

Carol starts to panic. The hotel resounds in a cacophony of torturous sounds. "Don't go! Don't leave me alone!"

"I need it, Carol! I'll only be gone half an hour. I promise."

"You won't make any other stops, not even to buy a newspaper?" She cries uncontrollably, as usual.

"No. I promise!" She watches him leave. She views him as completely unaware of her pain. She wishes she had his level of problem so she could exist in the world. Tomorrow is her session with Dr. Jastreboff and Dr. Gray. Her tests are all negative for required surgery.

The heater noise hits hard. It comes through the vents of the hotel like it always has, but to Carol, the sound is equivalent to the volume of an Amtrak train. Her auditory gain picks up ordinary sounds no human being can hear. It magnifies them to a killer degree. Hyperacusis has already chewed her up and spit her out. It's a monster with humongous teeth which is now chasing her all over the hotel room.

She estimates how many tablets she has in her suitcase. *Everyone expects too much of me! Who would want to live like this, or even try?*

"Help me!" she sobs as she looks at the tablets in her hand. *What can Dr. Jastreboff do tomorrow? There is no surgery—the test was negative again. I have to escape this pain. I need to be free of this torture. There are no tomorrows left. I have already suffered through as many todays as I can endure.*

Guiltily, she picks up the phone and dials Dr. Jastreboff. "He went out," Randie says.

"Did he go home? I need him quickly."

"No. I think he is outside someplace. Hold on, I'll give you Susan."

"Carol, are you there?" She hears Susan Gold's voice.

She knows Susan is an audiologist. She has talked long distance to her many times. Even though she has only met Susan this morning for a brief introduction before her testing, the whole tinnitus and hyperacusis staff are well aware of Carol. Fred thinks Carol is well known throughout the whole University of Maryland.

"You have to hang on until tomorrow, Carol. Dr. Jastreboff will help you. He'll be there for you tomorrow."

"But that doesn't do me any good now. I need him now, Susan, to be able to live until tomorrow."

She looks at the tablets. "I'm going to swallow all my tablets, Susan." She looks over at the bathroom, thinking about the shower that will turn into Niagara Falls in the morning.

Carol is so tired. She doesn't want to hurt anymore. She wonders if that is such an unreasonable request. She hears Susan's voice repeating, "Carol, promise me you'll take only one tablet—tell me that you'll take only one to calm you down. Do you hear what I'm saying, Carol?"

She is crying really hard now. She thinks of Dr. Jastreboff and all that has transpired between the two of them these past eight long months. *Can I do this to him? Right here in Baltimore? He cares about me so much. He'll think I'm selfish . . . to not consider his feelings.*

"Carol . . . are you there?"

"Yes, Susan. I promise I'll take only one. I'll meet you tomorrow for my appointment."

Carol always keeps her promises.

Dr. Jastreboff looks at Carol. She thinks he either has tears in his eyes or he recently came in contact with onions. She loves him dearly for his empathy. He introduces Dr. Gray, the medical doctor who works with him.

Dr. Gray asks questions and writes. Fred responds. Dr. Gray asks, "Did Carol act this way before these conditions?"

Fred describes Carol as obsessive and compulsive. He relates her past life activities to her present behavior. He talks to Dr. Jastreboff and Dr. Gray about his wife as if she has always been this way. He sloughs off his responsibility for her mental ward stay. "I was concerned for her depressive state. She couldn't sleep and wouldn't eat."

Carol still wants to end her suffering. Her pain was never from depression, and still is not from depression. Her agony is one of the cruelest of tortures that no one should ever have to endure.

Fred continues, describing what he believes was an obsession. "She used to work for many hours on her knitting without stopping."

Carol recalls Fred's words back home. "Do you agree to let me do the talking when we get to Baltimore? Dr. Jastreboff is a very busy man. I want to have some time with him, too, for my own problem. You have to get your points across quickly. You have to ask your questions in an organized fashion. I can do this for you. I can help you, if you'll let me."

She shuddered then. She shudders now, listening to the price she pays for Fred's help. He wins. He gets control of his wife. He has never before had this one-sided relationship with Carol. They both shared equally. They both tried to consider the other's wishes and desires. She always used to have a fifty-percent say.

He is describing my character falsely. He diagnoses what my sickness illustrates. Carol's actions make her seem emotionally ill, but she wasn't before this! Fred is attacking her with his words. She thinks he gets satisfaction—while she loses pride and virtue.

The afflictions cut like a knife. Fred adds salt to her wounds. He drains her emotionally. He makes her impossible task of living much worse than it already is.

Carol cries out for her deceased parents to help her. She idolized her father. Now she idolizes Dr. Jastreboff. Her mind thinks of both the Jastreboffs as the parents she wants so desperately to have back.

Fred's care can keep her alive. She needs to forge ahead despite his untrue statements. She feels betrayed and embarrassed. She needs to remain strong if she is to stay alive. She stores his harsh words as she stored her off-limit possessions in Texas. She wonders if she can ever forgive him. At the moment, his help outweighs the anger he aims directly at her—like a bullet advancing after the trigger is pulled.

Fred discusses me like I'm invisible. I am too sick and frightened to stop him. I can't stand up for my convictions.

Fred has leverage. He uses it in this room. Is he aware of how he is hurting me? He worries that there will be no time to discuss his auditory problem. How much more unfair can life be?

Why can't I defend myself? I need to tell my story the way it is, not the way Fred imagines it to be. I'm the one whose life is based on fact. They're listening to the wrong person—it's all wrong, so very wrong.

I work on something that I'm interested in for hours, like knitting a sweater. I might work twenty hours a day, until it's done. Who cares? It's my life! Does this make me what Fred calls me, "obsessive"? If there's a flaw, I rip it out. Sometimes I lose days fixing it. That's my decision. Is this a crime? I'm a perfectionist, not an "obsessivist"! Some people think I have creative talent.

Just because I make up my mind to do something and then do it in a hurry, is that bad, too? I decide that I've been poisoned, and so I immediately go to a detoxification center. I fly out the next day. Fred calls that compulsive. It was an act of desperation, not compulsion. The local doctors couldn't do anything to relieve my horrible symptoms. It took a lot of strength and determination to put myself through such tortures before realizing that they weren't actually helping.

Many similarly afflicted have accepted their doctors' statements that there's nothing they can do, that they'll just have to learn to live with it through medication and psychiatric counseling, if

173

necessary. And then many of them have given up and killed them-selves to escape the torture.

Why is Fred describing me in this way? Surely Dr. Jastreboff can see through Fred's words. He has to! I can't hang on without this wonderful doctor. But then I can't stay alive without Fred's help either.

Each minute of the days to come, my feelings of wanting to die have to "underride" my stronger emotions to stay alive. I have very little strength left. Do I have enough courage?

Dr. Jastreboff will be so proud of me if I can succeed. What is he counting on to keep me going? His generators? The former me who is gone? What Dr. Jastreboff thinks about me will always matter for the rest of my life.

Carol focuses back on Fred's voice describing her life in the past.

"Would you say that your wife had an anxiety problem before this condition? Did she take tranquilizers before?" Dr. Gray directs this question to Fred for an answer.

Why can't I speak for myself? I'm shaking my head "no," but I'm waiting for Fred to talk. Help me, God. Please, dear God, allow Dr. Jastreboff to save me!

Fred hesitates. He looks uncomfortable and embarrassed. *What about my past strengths, stabilities, and devotion?*

Finally, Carol hears her husband say, "No!" She feels vindicated. Her prison door opens. He has freed her of unfair labels.

"Let's take a break," Dr. Jastreboff announces. Everyone leaves. Carol stays seated.

She is surprised to hear Dr. Gray say, "I'm really sorry this happened to you!"

Dr. Gray explains to them both how the auditory system works. He examines Carol's ears. Her whole inner ear appears on a television screen. She prays for something wrong to show up. Dr. Gray says, "The tympanic membranes are intact and mobile with normal landmarks. There is no evidence of middle ear fluid, inflammation, or abnormal vascular masses."

Carol doesn't understand most of this, but she knows that Dr. Gray's knowledge is obviously much greater than the ear doctors she has previously seen. She translates his words into: "No surgery for you!"

Dr. Jastreboff spends hours discussing her test results and the severity of her condition. Afterwards he also discusses Fred's problem. He tells Fred, "You have hyperacusis, too! You need to wear the generators."

"He'll never wear them!" Carol says smugly.

"Oh, yes, I will!" Fred counters.

Dr. Jastreboff cites hypothetical situations to explain how the brain normally filters out all kinds of noise every day. Fred listens, fascinated. Carol only wonders if she can stay alive long enough to master her doctor's program.

"Take a crowded restaurant, for example," Dr. Jastreboff says. "You're barely able to hear your own voice and the people chatting at your table. You can't make out anything but a loud hum from all the others talking. Suddenly, from across the room, somebody says, 'Fred.' You hear 'Fred' as plain as day. This is because your brain has filtered out all the other sounds as being unimportant. But it knows instinctively that your name is definitely an important sound for you—you've always responded to it throughout your lifetime. So your brain broadcasts this sound loud and clear. It's up to you to then decide whether it is an important sound or not. You immediately look over to where the sound appears to have come from. You determine that your name was used for someone else and dismiss it as not being important in this instance.

"It is the same with the generators. Your brain at first gives importance to the quiet generator humming sound. Gradually, over a period of time, it is filtered out, along with the annoying tinnitus noises. Your brain will decide they are all unimportant sounds, and you will be able to 'habituate' them.

"This happens in the cortex of your brain. It is important that you refocus your attention away from the tinnitus. We try to counsel our patients to understand that tinnitus is only a small infraction of the auditory system. It's really nothing to be afraid of. It takes awhile, but gradually you will realize this. Your fear of the sounds tends to perpetuate their intensity."

Carol sits listening and shaking. Every part of her says, "I'm afraid! I'm afraid! I'm afraid of tinnitus and I'm afraid of hyperacusis."

Her brain responds, *"I thought so! Too bad for you, Carol! Great for me! With this attitude feeding your emotions, I'll just have to keep track of tinnitus now, won't I? Your fear just keeps me working overtime. I'll pay attention to tinnitus. I'll even track it round the clock, like the good little brain I am. Oh, boy! Oh, boy!"*

Dr. Jastreboff has used the word "habituate." This seems to be his key word of importance. Carol has studied this from her doctor's paperwork. With tinnitus, "habituate" means to ignore. Why is she dying if this is so simple? She needs to know now! She doesn't know what to ask.

"Ha! I do though," Mr. Know-It-All Brain adds. *"Why don't you ask your doctor how the heck you're supposed to ignore high-pitched squeals, thumping noises, banging noises, a sprinkler system in your head, and whatever else you have, huh, Carol?"*

Dr. Jastreboff continues, "First, though, we must get rid of the hyperacusis. Once you are able to listen to all the outer sounds in a normal manner again, your brain can start ignoring the tinnitus sounds."

"We'll see about that, won't we?" the nasty brain states.

One thing is certain. Carol will never not have negative feelings about tinnitus and hyperacusis. *"See . . . I knew it! I knew it!"* the happy brain brags. She also wonders, if this is her attitude, how will she ever get well? A faint portion of the brain strives to be heard. *"When Carol is able to use sound again, watch out! She will blast tinnitus to kingdom come. You'll see!"*

Fred asks, "What's the difference between my condition and Carol's?" *I can't believe he needs to ask! His is just a fraction of mine!*

Dr. Jastreboff replies, "Your wife has hyperacusis clear across the board. She cannot tolerate any sounds. You have specific high-frequency sounds that become amplified."

"The high-pitched sounds are very painful for me," Fred states. "Carol's voice is the worst."

That does it! Carol sits listening. She's furious at Fred for his comment about her voice. Then she listens to Dr. Jastreboff's explanation.

"Women's voices, and children's, too, have generally high-pitched tones. Your test results show that you are especially sensitive to high-frequency tones."

"Now that you mention it, the sound of children screeching is quite painful for me," Fred says.

Carol is thrilled to hear Dr. Jastreboff's explanation. Her wonderful doctor has both diagnosed Fred's problem and clarified the reason—all in one short sentence! Dr. Jastreboff is able to explain everything there is to know about sound. He turns to Carol. "Why don't you get started with Susan Gold, and I'll see you again in a little while."

Carol walks down the hall to Susan, trying to absorb all these facts. She just wants the hyperacusis to reverse itself. Next, she'll deal with the tinnitus. Then, she'll try to understand more. Right now, all she can handle is to be able to walk down the hallway of this Tinnitus and Hyperacusis Clinic in Baltimore, Maryland. And Fred!

Chapter 26

Susan Gold uses Dr. Jastreboff's skilled knowledge and methods. She has kept Carol alive for today's appointment. Her work is important and she's been kind to Carol. Carol wishes she lived in Baltimore. It would make her struggle a lot easier. The staff are familiar with what she's enduring. The rest of the world sure isn't! Carol listens attentively as Susan describes how the auditory system works.

Susan asks, "On a scale of 1 to 10, using 10 as the top severity, how would you describe your suffering with tinnitus? With hyperacusis?"

Carol doesn't need to think. "One million." *This questionnaire is useless to describe my level of pain. I'll never ever be on this scale for analyses. I could die from my anxiety alone!*

"Let me change your ear moldings." Carol removes the generators that she bought in San Francisco. "It's much better to have our open model."

"Oh, my gosh! I've been wearing these other ones for eight months. I probably didn't get any benefit at all from them. Have I wasted all this time?"

"No, no. It's okay, but this style will allow more sound to reach your auditory system."

"You mean, then I can possibly get well sooner?"

"We hope so! That's the idea."

Why didn't I find Dr. Jastreboff from the beginning? I was too sick to get the proper generator setup in Baltimore in the first place. I'm fighting against time. Only Dr. Jastreboff and I understand this.

Susan starts cutting tubing. She measures Carol's ears to make a comfortable fit.

"I'm wearing the generators round the clock, Susan. I'm sleeping in them. I can't hurt the tubing doing that, can I?"

"Not at all." Carol examines the new moldings in Susan's mirror. "Here are some extra setups. You should switch to them when the tubing becomes brittle. Your local audiologist can put the new ones on. It's not hard to do. Fred can even change them."

I don't think so! "How long do you think I can go before they need changing?"

"It's hard to say, because you're wearing them all the time. Most of our patients wear them for fewer hours each day."

"I don't have a choice, Susan. I need to have them on every minute."

"I know," Susan replies sympathetically. Carol gives her a long hug good-bye.

Carol sees Dr. Jastreboff in the hallway as she leaves Susan's office. She wants to find out what his prognosis is. She has to have this information to hang onto as her incentive to live through this agony.

"Dr. Jastreboff," she wipes away her tears with her hand. "When do you think I'll be all right?"

He hesitates as he looks at her. "Maybe by the end of the year. I can't say for sure . . . but the following year, you should be much better. The year after that for sure. I don't think I should make any more speculative guesses at this time."

Carol starts to count the months on her fingers. Eleven more months to go until the end of the year. Tears well up again in her eyes. She figures maybe 1997, but 1998 for sure. Her odds of making it are slim. Why isn't Dr. Jastreboff talking like they are? Can she actually live through this? He's so objective. He has very calmly told her what he knows will happen. But it will happen only if she stays alive. But how?

"What can I do to help myself?" She watches him thinking.

"Go to the zoo." He knows she loves animals, especially dogs, especially her dog, Peanut, that is gone.

I'll go to the zoo. I'll even mail him a monkey postcard from the San Francisco Zoo. I'll show everyone my old strength from yesteryear! She's all keyed up to lick this thing, despite yesterday's overwhelming thoughts of suicide.

"Can I go square dancing with Fred? He keeps asking me to."

"If you think you can. You should back off if the sounds bother you."

Dr. Jastreboff is very liberal. He wants everyone to be well and happy. He doesn't put limitations on what you should do. *He wants me to try to do whatever I think I can.*

"Please try to smile, and please try not to cry!" Carol listens to his words. She doesn't think she will ever not cry, let alone smile, but she'll keep trying. She walks over to him and grabs his hands.

"I don't know if I can manage, but I'll sure try." Tears slide down her face. He looks sympathetically into her tortured eyes.

"We'll stay in very close contact. Your case is very severe, but every sound that you now hear will gradually decrease in time." He gently releases Carol's grip. She watches as he lowers his hands toward the floor to illustrate how every sound in the world will drop in volume.

"I'm so afraid."

"It's better to know."

No it isn't! I don't want to know that every sound in the world is magnified a thousand times.

"I think you will be okay," he concludes. They say good-bye.

She immediately feels desolate, like she has lost her best friend. There is something mysterious about the generators that Dr. Jastreboff does not volunteer.

The next morning as she packs to leave Baltimore, Carol glumly listens to Fred. He has just returned from breakfast, which she cannot eat. Now he marvels at a change that has occurred.

"You know my ear that has been plugged up for more than five years? Well, it just became unplugged—and after less than one day on the generators! Not only that, yesterday I had to wear muffs over my earplugs to be able to eat breakfast in that diner near the clinic—it's so noisy with people talking and dishes clanging. Well just now, I was able to sit and eat breakfast with only the generators on. Isn't that great? It's like a miracle!"

Carol doesn't mean to feel jealous or annoyed by his good fortune, but she does. Fred has a different case from her own. Fred is wearing the generators thanks to *her* condition. He would never have been tested and diagnosed by Dr. Jastreboff if *she* hadn't been critically ill. He would never have found Dr. Jastreboff to even know about a treatment. Besides, she doesn't see Fred debilitated and eliminating anything from *his* life. Now he's bragging at how well he's doing in only one day. Of course, he said it took him only two days to habituate his minor case of tinnitus.

I, on the other hand, leave the same way I came—very close to death, and without the surgery I was counting heavily on to save myself. It's not fair!

Tears run from her eyes with each word that Fred utters. She does feel glad for him—it's just that she feels so sad for herself. To make her feel better, her mom would say, "You should be glad that Fred cares enough to help you. He gives you the very best of everything."

This time her mom's words ring positively true. She finally has the best medical help available. She also has the *only* medical help available that is correct for these conditions.

She tries to calm her fears. She will have the Jastreboffs for emotional support and strength, which she will need plenty of. They will be there for her. They are committed to saving her. She can count on them.

Carol does not know whether she agrees with Dr. Jastreboff's better-to-know statement regarding hyperacusis or not. She becomes more traumatized than she already is. She deliberately tries to touch as little as possible. A fork hitting a plate equals a chunk of cement crashing to the ground. The slightest movement resounds with overpowering volume.

From the moment she steps out of bed, she sees herself as a little doe in the jungle. The lion is out there to kill her if she makes herself known. She tries to be invisible. She tries to move silently, but it's impossible! Dr. Jastreboff wants her to "keep sound running" in her home.

In the past, she watched horror films on television and in theaters. Now she lives beyond the scariest horror movie ever made. It plays like a science-fiction story. It's not though. It's happening to Carol and to others like her! This is real life! Carol's house echoes her bloodcurdling cries.

"Fred! Help me! I can't find one of my generators. Oh, never mind. It was hiding under my pillow. The generator sound is cutting in and out!"

"Try to put up with it!" She doesn't listen to him, of course, and has her local audiologist send it away for repairs. She buys a spare one to use in its place, for added security.

She studies Dr. Jastreboff's technical papers again:

> Habituation is brought about by resetting or reprogramming neuronal networks involved in subcortical signal detection. The generators provide distraction to the nervous system so that the auditory system is able to 'habituate,' or ignore sounds that are not important. . . .

> Hyperacusis is the result of the brain 'turning up the gain' on healthy hair cells in the ear, after other hair cells have died.

These theories indicate that the auditory retraining takes place above the cochlea and below the cortex. This treatment can be successful regardless of the physical site of the damage or how it was caused.

The interpretation of Dr. Jastreboff's theories and treatment finally hits her like a ton of bricks. *I thought the generators were supposed to be my friends. They are reported to have a nice, pleasing way about them. They do for Fred, and I suppose they would for millions of others. Just not for me!*

Carol realizes what happens when an outside sound goes into an auditory system like her own. She has a gain—the volume is already turned way up, a thousand times up. Her system picks up everything that the average person cannot even detect. It not only picks it up, it blasts her away to kingdom come. But she never figured on the generators doing the same hideous thing!

Her hyperacusis is exceptionally severe and complex. Her auditory system turns up the generator sound because it is an outside sound just like all the other noises on the planet. Dr. Jastreboff knew. She didn't. Now she does!

Surprise, surprise! The generator sound is killing me, too! I screamed about the generators being too loud and the dial moving by osmosis. I thought they were malfunctioning! What an idiot I've been! That's what Dr. Jastreboff evidently decided not to tell me.

Carol finds out she has to tolerate every sound in the world magnified, including the treatment she has placed in her ears! She is in a state of shock from this revelation. *Dr. Jastreboff knew this from the very beginning. I won't have peace of mind from the generators until the gain starts decreasing. The generators have to chip away at the hyperacusis before I'm blown away from this agony. I'll never make it!*

How can my motivation possibly be strong enough to resist the agony being inflicted on me? Does Dr. Jastreboff think I will quit? If I quit, I'll die. He knows that. My stopping his treatment is the same as signing myself into the morgue.

She thinks more about suicide.

I can deliberately swallow too many pills and hope to die without living in worse shape. I can attempt to function in enough sound to drive my car to a bridge. Could I even bear the thunderous roar of traffic long enough to jump into the icy waters of the bay? With my luck and swimming skills, I'd probably survive that, too!

On the other hand, nothing will get better with my severe and awful tinnitus until the hyperacusis reverses. I hear multiple, ridiculous sounds, all doing crazy things at the same time. The outside sounds are slurred, and they mimic my tinnitus. This treatment will take way too long! Why me?

Chapter 27

It is said that God moves in mysterious ways. Is there a purpose for Carol having been afflicted to such a degree? If Dr. Jastreboff is able to help her complex condition, could it have been meant to be so that she can help him help others who are stricken?

There are some 250 million people in the world who have bits and pieces of what she has. Is she supposed to reach each and every one of them? How could she possibly do that?

If I recover, this is going to be my next obsession—to help ensure that no one will ever again have to endure my kind of pain and suffering. Nor will anyone have to kill himself to escape. She needs more answers. She phones her doctor in Baltimore.

"How was I supposed to know to listen to CNN that day, Dr. Jastreboff, when you were on TV two years ago? What if I had been home instead of out of the States, like I remember I was? I'd have seen you holding what looked like a hearing aid. I would have said, 'What do I need to watch this for? I have the most superpowered hearing in the world!' Then I would have flicked the remote to a scary horror story, the scarier the better!

"You should have said, 'Stop! Don't change the channel! This could affect you without your even being aware of it!' " Carol catches her breath. She waits for Dr. Jastreboff to comment on her statement.

"Give me a break. I'm only a scientist!" *Only?*

"I agree with you about the marketing, though." *He likes my ideas!*

She has another important question which she dreads asking. She hopes to be completely "normal." She wants her former self back. She can't live with noise for the rest of her life.

"Your scientific paperwork says that you have an eighty-five-percent success rate. You mean, I can only get eighty-five percent better, at the most?"

"No. That's not what that means. I've been able to help eighty-five percent of the people whom I've treated."

"So I can get completely well?"

"Yes!"

Carol is immensely relieved. She says good-bye to her doctor back East with hope in her heart.

She swallows a tablet to get through the night. *Hmmm . . . eighty-five-percent success rate. . . . Dr. Jastreboff is always so confident and positive. He even says, "You'll get well if you want to." Want to? What does that mean exactly? Wouldn't everyone want to? Why then is there any percent of no success?*

All the patients who come to Baltimore and who Dr. Jastreboff evaluates as needing generators leave with generators. Suppose they go home and don't use them consistently? How is anyone to know what patients do when they are on their own? What if they get embarrassed because they think the generators are an eyesore? I get embarrassed all the time. I wear hats when it's 100 degrees outside so people won't stare. I don't want people feeling sorry that I can't hear because they think I'm wearing hearing aids. I have perfect hearing, for God's sake!

Carol surmises that some patients do not follow Dr. Jastreboff's protocol exactly. She doesn't have a choice. She is fighting for her life. But she always follows doctors' instructions to the letter.

If I'm lucky enough to come out of this, I need Dr. Jastreboff to know that I am a good patient. I am not the awful, crying, complaining person I appear to be!

Fred would admonish Carol for what he views as horrible, unappreciative, even disrespectful questions. Carol knows, though, that Dr. Jastreboff doesn't view what she needs to understand as such. She respects Dr. Jastreboff. She would never intentionally be rude or rotten. Only her medical condition is rotten.

She just doesn't know why this has happened to her. She doesn't understand why Dr. Jastreboff was only on that one television station when she was on her way toward a horrible death. Carol had episodes: warning signs of what lay ahead. "Hyperacusis is a pre-tinnitus condition." These are Dr. Jastreboff's words. She is his proof.

"Can you stop tinnitus from happening if you recognize hyperacusic symptoms?" she asks her brilliant doctor.

"Maybe," he answers.

Hmmm. . . . It's too late for me, but I can warn others. Who would have believed her if she had understood then? Her mind flashes back to her symptoms. *If people become aware of what I so casually dismissed, maybe I can prevent this from happening to anyone else.*

Carol turns back the clock. . . . *She is with her friend returning from the fashion shows at the Louvre museum in Paris. She flies back to Mexico City with Fernando instead of going home. She has been in Athens and has toured the Greek islands. She feels guilty for taking extra side trips without Fred.* The spring showings always occur during tax season, so why should I feel guilty?

"Fernando!" She grabs her suitcase and deliberately drops it on the sidewalk.

"Will you stop worrying about the pink and turquoise leather, Carolina! It'll be on the next flight. I know you want to go back to the airport and sit there all day to wait for it. Ha, ha, ha!" Fernando and the taxi driver hoist luggage out of the trunk of the cab.

"*Fernando!*" *she yells again, backing away from her case where it has landed.* "*It's not the missing fabric; it's my case, my suitcase!*"

He looks at her suitcase. It's zipped. It's intact. He looks at her, questioningly.

"*Don't you hear it?*" *she asks.*

"*Hear what?*"

"*The bomb ticking.*"

"*You must be kidding!*"

"*No. Of course I'm not kidding! Why would I kid about something like that? Do you suppose someone got into my suitcase in Athens? Remember how we were questioned and searched? And all those guys standing with rifles guarding the airport? And that armored tank? A soldier was sitting in there, you know!*"

"*Carolina! You have such a vivid imagination. You're watching too much goofy stuff in your country!*"

You sound like my mother! "*Come on, admit it! You were scared in Athens, too!*"

"*But now we're in Mexico, Carolina.*" *He looks at her, laughing, and says,* "*We're in my country now, where it's safe!*"

Are you kidding! That's sure debatable! Carol wants to hash this out in the future. She knows Mexico well. She's no longer a "turista."

"*Fernando, I'm not going near my suitcase! Do you hear me?*"

"*Do you want your clothes or not? You can always walk down the street naked. Ha, ha, ha.*" *He laughs at his little joke.* "*You will have all these gorgeous Mexicans looking at you.*" *He is still laughing as they enter his apartment building.*

Carol doesn't laugh. She watches her suitcase like a hawk as it's placed in the elevator. The doorman chats with Fernando. Carol's complaints are dismissed.

She is exhausted from their trip. She is a guest in her friend's country. She stays in many of his family's homes where she studies advanced Spanish and the fashion business. Could it be that she's so tired that she is hearing things that aren't actually there?

The elevator ascends. **The tick, tick, ticking** *from her luggage grows louder. They enter the condo.*

"Aren't you ever going to open up your suitcase?" Fernando tries to keep a straight face. She hears him snickering. *"Ha, ha. I'll do it for you."* Carol goes to the far side of the living room.

"See, there's nothing here." He unzips the case and pulls back the lid. *"Come on over and look for yourself."* He motions with his hand. Carol cowers with apprehension.

She sits on the floor in the far corner of the room debating what to do.

"My mother should only see how you pack, Carolina. She wouldn't allow me to associate with you. Ha, ha, ha, ha." Fernando laughs at all his humor in English. *"Don't you want to change your clothes? Ha, ha. Juanita will be here any minute."*

Juanita works for Fernando. Carol would love to have her job, only Carol lives in the United States. She'd have to live in Mexico to do the kind of work she enjoys so much. Fred thinks Carol already lives in Mexico. She is always gone far too long.

In a short time, Fernando will have a quota from his government. Then Carol will seek out U.S. companies for his factory to do manufacturing. His "maquiladores" have sewn for London Fog and other well-known U.S. fashion houses.

Carol feels very lucky this particular year. Her friend brings this good luck. They have escaped "unhurt" from their Bermuda accident only a few days before. Her business venture with Fernando will rapidly expand in the States. The future looks very exciting. The fashion world alone is exciting. Only this potential "bomb threat" is unexciting—it's frightening!

"There's absolutely nothing in your case that looks suspicious. My God, did you know you stole a hotel beach towel from Bermuda? No wonder you have such a mess! Ha, ha, ha."

Carol inches closer to where Fernando stands so bravely. She hears the **tick, tick, tick.** Why doesn't he hear it? *She inhales deeply. She starts to toss things out of her bag. She looks. She searches. Nothing seems amiss, but she is getting closer—the ticking is getting louder! Now there is only one thing left in the suitcase—her cosmetics case. Everything else is spread out all over the carpet. She eyes it suspiciously.*

"It's in there! I know it is!"

*Fernando walks away. 'Where are you going, Fernando? I
need you to stand right here." She motions at her side. She isn't
capable of being that brave all by herself.*

*"I've got work to do," he responds, as if his little fun time is
all used up. He shuffles through his briefcase.*

*Fernando has forced her to investigate alone. He thinks she's
acting silly again. I'll show him I'm not a little baby.*

*She grabs her cosmetics case. She tosses it on the carpet away
from her. She slowly creeps up and unzips it a crack. Then she
backs up and waits. She approaches it again, unzips it all the way
and tosses it upside down.*

*She yells out with relief and joy! "It was only my teensy-
weensy alarm clock the whole time!" That's odd. Why couldn't
Fernando hear it like I did?*

*She'll never live this one down. She has just given him one
more thing to laugh at and tease her about. He kids her constantly.
Now the teasing will surely increase.*

*Carol wishes that she had a crystal ball. She knows it would
foretell how wonderful their business venture will be, especially
since her "bomb" was just an inch-and-a-half-long Seiko alarm
clock.*

Carol dabs at her eyes. She had struggled so hard to discover the reason for her condition. She had tried so many
wrong treatments. She had taken the causes of tinnitus from
textbooks and attempted to cure herself with reported methods.
She did many dangerous, torturous things to herself, jeopardiz-
ing her health.

She starts to imagine her symptoms and Dr. Jastreboff's
treatment as a sort of puzzle and game. She sees it as one that
can be purchased in the store and then played. She parallels living through the treatment by moving a marker on the board—
except the game she plays is for her life!

Now she understands the symptoms. Her puzzle begins to
take shape. The pieces fit together and start to form a picture.

She sees it as an ugly one, one that needs to be separated and reassembled.

Her symptoms of tinnitus and hyperacusis are all too clear to her now. She had beaten her head against a stone wall. She had punished herself for not realizing. If she had known, whom could she have told? Who would have believed her?

No one believed her when her condition exploded. What makes her think if she had recognized the symptoms, it would have been any different? How do you get help if no one knows what you are asking to get help for?

Dr. Jastreboff is the only correct doctor for me in the entire world. He is like finding a needle in a haystack. This is not fair!

"Life is not always just and fair, Carol," Dr. Jastreboff says.

"It's hard enough without tinnitus and hyperacusis," she responds.

"You will, one day, go back to all of life's other little problems, those other than from tinnitus and hyperacusis," he assures her.

I can't wait! But never will I forget this kind of suffering!

Symptoms for medical conditions are supposed to be documented in textbooks, along with their treatments. Her own actions portrayed warning signs years ago when she was well. These overlooked signs have finally erupted into sirens blasting through her ears. All because of lack of knowledge.

She hears Dr. Jastreboff's words: "What happened has already happened."

This is true, but I will not let it go.

Her recollections are clues in this vicious game she plays. They verify Dr. Jastreboff's specialized skill and knowledge. His treatment and theories are true. They illustrate the complete recovery that is possible. *Oh, my God! My memories illustrate symptoms of tinnitus and hyperacusis that I thought at the time were all puzzling and peculiar actions!*

Chapter 28

Carol is back home in California trying to fight through time. She is desperate to stay alive. The generators will require a lot of time to work on her brain and auditory system. "Refocus your attention. You'll be helped quicker," Dr. Jastreboff has told her.

"Refocusing," the most important card in the game for her life. *Think back. He wants you to refocus.* . . . Carol swallows her drugs. She gets drowsy. She wills her mind off her present pain like her doctor wants her to do. She returns to play her game. Carol draws a clue card. "Remember how many chances you had. They were your symptoms. They were there all the time. . . ."

"Action"—The scene unfolds. . . .

"If anything happens to me, stay away from my brother, Carolina!" Fernando sounds serious. There is no laugh.

"I will!" Carol doesn't understand Fernando's warning. Carol is married. She believes in the sanctity of marriage.

Three years later, Carol is in the American Embassy in Guadalajara. This is Roberto's hangout. Roberto is Fernando's brother. She still cries over the death of her good friend. Acquired Immune Deficiency Syndrome has hit the fashion industry hard. Carol is happy Roberto has a girlfriend, Felicia.

"Let's make a toast to our business venture. Okay?" Roberto says. He raises his glass and yells, "Bring more tequila!"

The waiter dashes over. He looks at Carol. "What would the American like?" Felicia and Roberto wait for her response.

"I can't drink that stuff. Do you want me to get sick all over your sister's house? Besides I like only sweet drinks."

"Sweet like you, right?" Roberto says. "Ha, ha, ha." Carol looks over at him with a creepy feeling. She wonders about the brother's sincerity, the brother whom Fernando had warned her about. "Lemon and lime soda, will you drink that?"

"Yes," she replies.

The waiter brings a bottle of soda and a glass. Roberto pours a little tequila into the glass. He adds the lime soda. "Try it. Just take a sip."

"It's delicious. It's pretty sweet mixed with the lemon and lime."

"See?" Roberto says. "You have to learn to trust me." He laughs. "Fernando is no longer around to protect you." He continues laughing.

Carol doesn't think he is funny. She grieves for her friend. She works skeptically now with the wrong brother in the fashion industry, still not understanding Fernando's warning. She wants to forget the pain of his death and the remembering. She can't, though.

She's thirsty. She drinks the whole glassful of tequila and asks for a refill.

"It's all those tacos de lengua. Ugh, ha, ha, ha. How can you eat that stuff? You should be eating hamburgers, like we are. Are you sure you don't want one?" Roberto asks.

"They do look good—for Mexico, that is." Now she is the joker. She laughs at Roberto's expression. Felicia remains silent as they banter back and forth.

"I love tongue tacos with your hot sauce. I'm just thirsty now, really thirsty. I overate like I always do," she explains. They eat, and Carol drinks. Roberto and Felicia drive Carol to Terisita's house. Terisita was Fernando's favorite sister.

"Gosh, I'm really dizzy," Carol confesses, as she climbs down from the company van. "Thanks. See you tomorrow." She starts to press the buzzer on the gate. Roberto hops over and intervenes.

"You should be drunk with all that tequila you had," Roberto laughingly says. "Let me get the gate for you."

"No, thanks. I'm fine. Good-night."

Rosa, the woman who raised Fernando, hurries over to let her in. She speaks Spanish rapidly, but Carol understands everything she says. Carol talks to her all the way on the walk through the gardens to the house, and then all the way up the winding staircase. Carol is not really drunk, just light-headed. Her Spanish usage is perfect with Rosa. They discuss the leftover enchiladas and chilies that Carol loves and had stuffed herself with at lunch.

Carol walks into her bedroom. She looks over at the shower stall. She wonders if another shower would make her fall asleep quicker. She needs to sleep. The memories of Fernando are so painful.

She walks to the window. She looks down at the swimming pool. The pool is centered directly in front of the second house on the property—Fernando's house, the one he designed so carefully. She remembers touring through the bare foundation years ago. "See, my swimming pool will run the length of the house, Carolina. Do you like my designs?"

Carol looks up at the stars. They seem to be twinkling just for her. She wipes away the tears that are falling. She thinks of her deceased friend while she stands at the window in one of his homes. Does Fernando know that she's here? She wants him to understand that finally she is doing the work he had wanted her to do with his company.

Suddenly, she's startled. My gosh! There's something out there attracting thousands of birds. Roberto never cleans the pool. Maybe bird food is attracting the swarms that she hears.

She looks carefully around for sight of the birds. She grabs some tissues and starts wiping the inside of the window, but it's already clean. What did she expect? The family employs so much help. Surely the maids wouldn't overlook the windows!

Carol covers her ears with her hands. The tweeting is very loud. How come she sees only one little bird? Is it possible that swarms of birds have descended on this piece of property just like they did on Bodega Bay in that Hitchcock movie, The Birds? *Is she drunk like Roberto suggested? She guesses she is a little woozy. She yawns and lies down.*

Wait until she tells Fred that she got tipsy right here, back where she first came to visit . . . so long ago. . . . Why did Fernando have to die?

Carol falls asleep. She wants to forget her painful memories. The birds will be forgotten, too. She has so much manufacturing work to do. Carol doesn't suspect her exciting and lucrative career will soon be completely destroyed, along with her life! She has no idea that she will almost be terminally ill in only one year's time. How could she have? She is so healthy right now!

Why didn't she check into her idiosyncrasies? Carol hears her own voice answer. She hears her deceased mother answer. She hears Fred answer. Finally, she hears Dr. Jastreboff say, as in unison, "How could anyone have known?" Somehow, she can't unload the guilt.

"My God, Fred, I used to be able to hear my own wristwatch ticking without holding it up to my ear." She always slept on the far side of their king-size bed. The triple dresser was five feet from the bed. The small alarm clock sat there, **tick, tick, ticking.** She had heard those seconds ticking off for years.

"No wonder I couldn't fall asleep for hours," Carol cries out in horror. She remembers . . . it's all coming back . . . it all adds up now . . . but it only makes her feel worse.

Every day for four years following her accident, it was always, "Carol! Now I'm going to be late again! If you're going to unplug the alarm clock, at least plug it back in." Carol thinks back to her inconsiderate ways. She didn't mean them. She didn't understand them. She used to disconnect the clock almost nightly. It was an unconscious gesture. It was an automatic gesture. She was protecting herself from sound. Now she is dying from sound.

"It wasn't only the clock, Carol," her husband wants her to admit. "You used to unplug all the appliances in our bathroom. You said they were humming even though their switches were turned off." She remembers Fred's comments: "My electric toothbrush is dead! My Water Pik no longer squirts!"

She used to giggle. She used to be sneaky. She would get up early and replug his possessions when he wasn't looking.

"The jury finds you guilty," the judge says.

Carol collapses on the floor. "I can't stand this torture! Why won't anyone help me die?"

Carol calls Baltimore. "I can't make it!" she screams out to everyone!

Randie says, "Do whatever it takes!"

Susan says, "We know how strong you are—just ride it out!"

Dr. Jastreboff wants her to live. He says, "I want you to find a psychiatrist. You need to seek out a smart one. You need to find one who is knowledgeable about drugs."

"How will I know when I have a smart one?" She doesn't wait for Dr. Jastreboff's response. She always talks too much. She continues. "I hate psychiatrists. They won't understand my problem. They'll think I'm crazy. They'll think I'm imagining my condition," she sobs to her doctor in Baltimore.

"It doesn't matter what they think. In fact, it's better if they don't understand your condition. Just let them analyze your emotions and actions. Let them prescribe a medication. Let them do a psychological report on you. I will read what they say. I will see what drug they prescribe."

Carol understands that Dr. Jastreboff knows there are medications that will assist her over the crises with her condition. She promises to find a smart psychiatrist. *There probably is no such animal, but for you, Dr. Jastreboff, I'll try!*

The player looks at the game. Carol learns the rules quickly. "How do you know when you have won?" she wants to know. The rules are quite explicit. "You win when you have lived enough time to allow your treatment to alleviate your pain. By hard work, you will have conquered tinnitus and hyperacusis," Dr. Jastreboff would say.

"Can't I use a good MD to help me the same way a psychiatrist can?" Carol asks Dr. Jastreboff.

"Yes, if you can find a smart one. Psychiatrists work with drugs. We're looking for someone skilled in this area." She knows her present MD does not meet Dr. Jastreboff's requirements. *But who does?* If she's to stay alive long enough to experience a hyperacusis reversal, she must live off the very thing she hates the most—pills!

Fred finds "him." In the psychiatrist's office, the doctor says, "I know what your suffering is all about." He gives her two tablets to choose from. He reads her the side effects. Both pills are antidepressant medications.

Carol is not depressed. She may want to kill herself but she is not depressed! Her pride feels injured. Her condition is not humanly possible to live through. No one in the world has ever lived through this complexity of tinnitus and hyperacusis. *The good psychiatrist doesn't have the foggiest idea what my suffering is about. Neither does Fred!* She is attempting to hang on for only one person: Dr. Jastreboff. He is her incentive. His time and patience with her are driving her on. He is the reason she has tried this psychiatrist.

In the car going home, Fred is mad at Carol. "You're not even going to try these pills, are you?"

"I may. No. I won't! I can't even swallow water without pain. I will not start swallowing a drug for a condition I don't have. The tranquilizers hurt enough going down. I will not subject myself to any more pain than I already have!" *I did good!*

Dr. Jastreboff wants her to keep eating. He wants her to stay alive. "If you really want to help me, I need a carton of cottage cheese. I'll try to get something down," she says to her husband.

"Okay. We're near Safeway."

"No. No! I need the brand from Lucky's!" she adamantly insists. She starts to cry. Fred still can't understand what she has to deal with. She gets his sympathy rarely.

"Okay. I'll go to Lucky's to get your cottage cheese," he angrily replies.

Carol knows it's tax season. Fred is pressured with work. He drives to psychiatrists whom she has no intention of listening to.

"Why don't you see a stomach specialist?" he annoyingly asks.

"I hate all doctors. Besides, you know that the stomach doctor here in town knows me. He'll never believe anything I say. I'll go to him and you can see for yourself." Carol shudders at the thought of the stomach specialist. *I'll subject myself to the gastrointestinal doctor for you, Dr. Jastreboff.*

Suddenly, sirens blare. Lights flash behind them. She puts on her headset and starts to sniffle. Fred swears under his breath. It's too late! The policeman writes as he walks.

"Do you know that you went through a 'No Left Turn' sign?" the uniformed officer asks, as he continues to write. "May I see your driver's license and registration, please."

"My wife is very ill and that sign is obscured, officer," Fred politely rebuts. "When was that sign installed? I'm only turning here because she needs a certain kind of cottage cheese to eat!" Fred's excuses are wonderful! They are also to no avail. He is handed a sizable traffic violation. The policeman leaves. Carol feels Fred's anger, and it is directed at her. Fred turns to his poor, sick wife.

"This is all your fault. If you didn't need a specific brand of cottage cheese at a specific store, I never would have turned here." She hates him again—cottage cheese and all!

They pull into the supermarket driveway while Fred continues to rant about what he has to put up with. She cries, "I wish I were dead!" She looks out the car window. Suddenly, she sees a young woman who is obese. She watches the woman walk with difficulty. "I wish I were her instead of me."

Fred looks over in Carol's direction. "You've got to be kidding!"

No, she is not kidding. The woman can lose weight if she wants to. Carol wants to live, but wanting and trying just aren't enough. The hope she feels in her heart of surviving is very minute. Again she wonders, *Is Dr. Jastreboff's influence on me strong enough to pull me through?*

Chapter 29

Carol reads her new *Hyperacusis Bulletin*. She tries to be open-minded. The information is only the opinion of the editor. *He is wrong.*

Dr. Rosenberg, the internist in New Jersey, is dead. The bulletin clearly states that he obviously had more than tinnitus and hyperacusis.

She sobs hysterically. What could be more? There is no more as far as she is concerned. These afflictions are enough by themselves. He killed himself to escape the tortures. He was debilitated. He was suffering. "God, please help me!" Her screams pierce the night!

She can't stop crying. If only she hadn't taken offense at Dr. Rosenberg's abruptness. If only he had talked to her, opened up to her. She has to find out the truth. She calls his house.

"Is your mother there?" Carol asks a young girl.

"No. May I take a message please?"

"What's your name? How old are you?" Carol must know.

"My name is Sarah. I'm fifteen."

"Sarah, I'm the woman who called a couple of months ago. I talked to your father. I'm critically ill with the same condition." *I wish he had let me help and not said he was too busy to talk to me.*

"I remember when you called. I can have my mother call you back when she gets home."

"Yes, please do. I need to talk to her. I want to talk to her very much. Sarah . . ." Carol pauses. She wipes her nose, which is running profusely. "Sarah," she starts again. "Was your father sick from something other than hyperacusis?"

"No!" The no comes out definitely and decisively. There is no mistaking the horrible finality of what Carol hears from the doctor's young daughter.

"But the bulletin—I just read, I mean, it indicated that he might have had another illness, something physically terminal."

"No. He didn't. He cut his carotid artery because of his hyperacusis."

Carol shakes uncontrollably. "Dear God!" she says out loud. *I was horrible to ask her!* "Are you okay, Sarah? I didn't mean to upset you more! I'm sorry! I'm so sorry!"

"No, it's all right. We're okay now. I'll have my mom call you."

"Thank you, Sarah."

Carol is not okay. In fact, she is far from okay. She made it through the call, but she won't make it through the night. Her sobs turn to anger. She is mad at the people Dr. Rosenberg had turned to for help. Why hadn't someone helped him? Why hadn't he been saved? Could it be that he didn't have the energy left to endure any more suffering? But there could have been a happier ending to his torture. There was the promise of a normal life from Dr. Jastreboff.

She hurts too much from his death. She hurts too much from her own condition. Carol is in the very beginning of her treatment. She fears what Dr. Rosenberg did as a final solution for herself. There is only one person who can reassure her now, and she needs to talk to him immediately!

"Hold on. Don't hang up! I'll come right back. I'm on the phone to Europe. I'll tell them I'll talk to them later," he says reassuringly.

Carol sobs hysterically. Dr. Jastreboff can't understand her words because of her crying. "A doctor . . . an MD, Dr. Elliot Rosenberg . . . he . . . he committed suicide!" she cries out in anguish to Dr. Jastreboff.

"You have to stop crying and try to calm down. It's done. You need to be okay. This is what is important!"

Why doesn't he sound surprised over this death? How many suffering people out there are killing themselves every day? He knows this is happening. She tries to catch her breath.

"His name, it sounds familiar," she hears Dr. Jastreboff say through her screams. "Are you all right now?"

He sounds so concerned about me. Dear God! Whose fault is this? I have to figure this out! "Why did he have to die? Why wouldn't he let you help him?" She sobs her heart out. She knows he's hanging on with her to make sure she'll be all right.

"I can't make everyone believe me." Dr. Jastreboff sounds sad and tired.

Carol hears the caring in his voice. She feels his empathy for all those who suffer. She is sick over Dr. Rosenberg's death. She is sick over others who may have done the same thing. She hurts for his family, and she hurts for herself. *I have to live to tell my story. I will!* She wants to avenge the death of this doctor. She wants to right the wrong that is happening. She has so many things she must do regarding these afflictions. She will do them in Dr. Rosenberg's memory. She hasn't decided how yet, but she knows that she will!

Carol talks to the doctor's wife, Jody Rosenberg. "He couldn't get help from his own colleagues," his wife tells her. Carol also talks to Dr. Rosenberg's good friend in Florida.

"He tried to sit on the patio with me. He tried to figure out what to do. He was intelligent. He had a lucrative medical practice. He was forced to run from sound."

"Forced to run from the world," Carol adds.

She discovers the irony of Dr. Rosenberg's tragic death. Dr. Rosenberg's parents had already arranged an appointment for him to see Dr. Jastreboff. It was scheduled for the day following his demise. Carol pieces together everything she is told. She visualizes. . . .

Dr. Rosenberg is in his car. He needs to get gas. It was once an easy task. Now nothing is. Tomorrow he is scheduled to drive a long distance with his family to see a neuroscientist who is supposed to be able to help him. His family promises a lot of rest stops along the way. He feels their love. But his torture from the freeway and engines that will explode in his ears overshadows everything.

He is on a local street with so much pain. He cannot cope with filling up his gasoline tank. Others all around him smile. They are oblivious to the world in which he lives. He is in a private hell.

He firmly grips the handle of the gas hose as the noise engulfs him. The magnified volume strangles him with every move he makes. Gas stations are noisy. It's funny, he never noticed before. He never heard bells clang and sirens screech. Not from gasoline tanks. He never cared when cars drove by or airplanes were high in the sky.

He has to make it home, but it's not possible. It's not within his tolerance. He has no more strength. He has no more joy. He has nothing left to offer.

He needs to keep his pride and dignity. He will and he does, as he severs his life. . . .

"Hi ya, kiddo. Is your tinnitus any better?" Jim wants to know.

"It takes a long time," she tries to explain.

"You need my medical doctor," he tells her again.

"I'm not supposed to try to measure what the generators are doing. It's a long-term treatment. I can't report progress on a daily basis. Dr. Jastreboff has repeatedly said to me, 'Don't talk about tinnitus!' I happen to know that Dr. Jastreboff even said to Mr. William Shatner, 'Don't talk about tinnitus for the next three months!' "

"Come on—do you expect me to believe that? William Shatner, the movie star? Who saved your life anyway by giving you Dr. Jastreboff?"

Jim thinks Carol is making up instructions from Dr. Jastreboff. She explains, "The generators work off the brain. They retrain the auditory system. They teach the auditory system not to pay attention to tinnitus. If I keep paying attention to it with you, I'm not allowing the generators to work. I'm defeating the purpose of this treatment."

She'd like to tell him more. *If the generators don't have a fighting chance to work because of something wrong I'm doing, why am I living through this torture? What's the sense of Dr. Jastreboff helping me?* She wants to be honest with Jim, but he doesn't believe what she already has said. He surely won't believe anything more.

He thinks she fabricates what she says, just like Fred does, about the extent of her condition, except that Fred also agrees that she shouldn't mention tinnitus. He heard Dr. Jastreboff's instructions, too!

Jim's response sadly confirms what she must do. He doesn't realize she's fighting for her life. If Fred doesn't realize it, how can she expect Jim to? Jim forces her not to talk to him anymore. She must eliminate contact with him to save herself. She feels badly about her decision. It's necessary though, if she is to get well.

If I don't do everything that Dr. Jastreboff advises, I'm wasting his time, efforts, and caring for my well-being.

Carol needs friends now who will understand her situation. Bernice misinterprets her actions and has deserted her. Sylvia and Helen live many miles away. Sylvia doesn't grasp her condition either. Who would? But she remains a loyal friend. She faxes Carol her artistic designs to cheer her up, but Carol is afraid to walk to the fax machine to get them. Helen is frequently confused as a result of her getting on in years.

First, Carol pleads for Fred to help, but he isn't able to. Next, she tells Celia and Helen she can no longer live. Then, she makes Arabella feel sad by crying about her agony. After this, she phones Bethann to say she will soon be dead. Finally, she sobs hysterically to Drs. Pawel and Margaret Jastreboff. She has had a busy phone morning.

Her routine rarely changes. Only the clocks keep **tick, tick, ticking.** It seems like all the clocks in the world have united in volume against her. She is totally debilitated. She cannot buy groceries. She cannot go to malls. She can no longer even walk on the street.

She looks again at the *Hyperacusis Bulletin*. She reads the story that shows the most suffering. She wonders if what she reads is true. She needs to find out how sick this woman really is. She dials Miami, Oklahoma.

The voice on the other end says, "Hello."

"Is this Ruth Rasor?"

"Yes."

"Hi. My name is Carol." Instantly, she has found a fellow sufferer.

Carol listens to the other woman's painful story. She understands it all too well. Ruth says, "The car hit mine from the front."

Carol interrupts her. "What kind of car were you driving?"

"A new Lincoln Continental." *A heavy new car, a large car, a strong car. And yet, this still happened?*

Ruth goes on, "The air bags inflated from the impact of the crash. The noise sounded like an atom bomb had exploded. The policeman came around to see if I was all right. I put my hands over my ears. I found that I couldn't understand or tolerate his voice."

Carol knows the rest by heart. After the crash, Ruth started crying. She lived through her accident, yet she has already died a thousand times over, like Carol has. Ruth's life was destroyed. She hadn't known what was wrong. She thought her heart would give out. *Ruth is alive only because of Dr. Pawel J. Jastreboff!*

"The ear, nose, and throat specialist in Tulsa prescribed niacin, low sodium, and reduced caffeine."

"You're kidding! My gosh!" But why should this surprise Carol? How many people mistakenly think these things affect the ears? Carol herself had been overdosed with niacin. As for the low sodium and reduced caffeine, the professionals at the poison center had even eliminated her toilet paper!

Ruth continues, "The doctor at the Oregon Research Center put me on Xanax. I was just hanging onto my life by a thread. I was in the emergency room of our hospital, and the doctors didn't know what to do. If my husband hadn't received a phone call from a friend who had read Dan Malcore's article in *Prevention* magazine, I'd never have found Dr. Jastreboff. My husband Bob called Baltimore because it was mentioned in that article. I was actually in about 160 to 170 decibels of sound from the airbags exploding. The blast was incredible!"

"Oh, my God!" Carol's eyes begin to tear. She tries not to cry. She tries to picture what Ruth is saying.

"We have a ranch in Oklahoma. Bob raises cattle and has horses that he races. Anyway, I didn't know what was wrong. I got on an airplane with Bob, shaking like a leaf. I look back now and don't know how I lasted. We flew to one of his races in Los Angeles. I stayed in the hotel up until the last possible minute. Then I went to the racetrack."

Carol doesn't need to ask Ruth why she had taken the trip to a racetrack. She shudders at the thought of it. She understands everything. Ruth was trying to do what she had always done. Ruth is afraid all the time, just like she is. Ruth has the trauma—it comes with hyperacusis—and it sticks around like butter to popcorn.

Carol thinks her condition is something a human cannot survive. She isn't human anymore. She doesn't know if she ever will be human again. She has changed . . . like vampires do.

Dr. Jastreboff says she's human. Carol doesn't have to question Ruth as to whether she feels the same inhuman way. Instead, Carol asks, "How long did it take before you found Dr. Jastreboff?"

"Eleven months!"

"That's awful! It took me even longer. I went a year and seven months!" Carol angrily exclaims.

"I don't know how you did it!"

"It was a horror! It was just like a bad dream that wouldn't end. I kept searching and searching for 'my' Dr. Jastreboff. This is absolutely crazy. We are debilitated and suffering so torturously and horrendously, and nobody in the whole world even knows about this condition. The doctors are our worst enemies because they lack knowledge in this field."

"I know," Carol hears her new friend sadly agree.

"Did anybody in your town humiliate you by not believing what happened to you?" Carol wants to compare scenarios.

"Bob printed flyers explaining my condition. He distributed them here in Miami where we live. Our town is small. Tulsa is a lot larger."

"The flyer idea is really clever." Carol knows Fred would be impressed and say that Ruth's husband is pretty sharp.

"In your case, Ruth, you had definitive symptoms at the time of your accident. Yet no one could help you. How horrible! It's really hard to believe!"

"I know."

"In my case, how was I, Fred, or anyone able to relate my condition back to an accident four years earlier? Thank God for Dr. Jastreboff! Isn't he wonderful? He and his wife are absolutely fantastic to their patients. I love them both!"

"Yes they are—I agree with everything. I don't even want to think what would've happened to me if our friend from church hadn't called Bob."

"Ruth, these hearing organizations are really misinformed and not knowledgeable about tinnitus and hyperacusis. The professionals working in this field all over the world are injuring patients by not referring sufferers to Dr. Jastreboff. How many more lives will be lost until this changes? This monster affliction, hyperacusis—this thing—it's not human! I told Dr. Jastreboff this."

"It isn't!"

"It's bad enough that hyperacusis feels supernatural. That isn't enough. It has to make us act like beings from another world. Someone should make a full-scale movie portraying this 'out-of-body' experience. Only then will people be able to understand it. Everyone needs to know the symptoms, the possible causes, and the treatment . . . because it could happen to them, too!

"A movie that illustrates hyperacusis would be scarier than anything that has ever been done before. Can you see it now? It would make Freddie Krueger in *Nightmare on Elm Street* look like a pussycat! Can you imagine what a sound company could do with a theme on this subject? The best part of the movie is that it would not only entertain but also educate.

"I really don't know if I'm going to live to tell people what happened. I'm in so much pain with this esophagus and digestive spin-off. I let the doctors do too much. Just living is an ordeal for me!"

"You're going to make it, Carol. You're going to survive to tell about this!"

"I don't know, Ruth."

"I'm going to pray for you, Carol."

"I need all the prayers I can get. If I do come out of this, I'll do plenty!"

"Good for you, Carol!"

Ruth thanks Carol for calling. They have missed meeting each other in Dr. Jastreboff's office by only a few days. They promise to keep calling and writing. They will help each other. They are already friends. Carol knows Ruth is a wonderful person. She hopes she will live to be able to meet her in person.

Chapter 30

"If you don't go to this square dancing class with me, our marriage doesn't have a chance of surviving. Besides, you need to get out of the house. You need to get your mind on something else," Fred says.

Carol contemplates only the part of Fred's threats that reflect Dr. Jastreboff's exact words: "Refocus your attention. You'll get well quicker." *The generator treatment needs my mind on something else, very badly.*

She listens to Fred elaborate. "This is something fun we can do together. Maybe you'll catch up to me in a year or so."

If I'm alive in a year.

"Maybe we can go as partners to hoedowns and on weekend trips. It could be fun."

"I don't know if I can cope with enough sound to be able to even get to the dance, Fred!"

"I think the music will be all right. The room is small, so you might be able to manage," Fred responds.

He overlooks her intense suffering from the ride in the car—the sound of air conditioning, tires on the roadway, cars on the freeway—the decibels of sound are painfully high in road traffic.

She is totally dependent on Fred for her existence. She compares her traumatized state to one of shell shock. She fights to exist from moment to moment with sound in her house. Now she feels threatened to partake in an outside activity—or else what, she wants to know?

Dr. Jastreboff tells her in Baltimore that she can try square dancing. She wonders whether he might say it's okay to go in a spacecraft to the moon, if she so desires. She can wear an ugly headset if necessary. She has to not care what others might think as they stare in disbelief.

Carol decides to try the dancing. It appears to be a less frightening alternative than staying home alone and living alone.

Fred moves heaven and earth to get home at the scheduled time. He honks the horn to pick her up. Only she is not ready. Hyperacusis stifles functioning, let alone speedy functioning.

"I don't know why you couldn't be on time. You had the whole day to get ready!"

You're a monster! You're mean! He belittles her fears and pain. She is miserable around him as much as she is in sound. His car is a torturous beast. The air conditioning reminds her of a jet ski skimming the water. She shakes as the sweat from fear drips down her body. She hears every external sound blast in pounding drumbeats as it synchronizes with her tinnitus.

In the dance hall, people smile and laugh. Carol cowers in terror. She pulls her hat down to cover the instruments that she wears. She is suddenly cold, so very cold.

"Do you have to wear those gloves?" Fred asks. "Who cares if your hands are cold!"

"I do! I care about everything!" she cries.

The music is pretty. The dancing is fun. Fred is an excellent dancer, but he acts as impossible as her medical condition is.

"Do you have to hang onto my hand so tightly?" he annoyingly says. She is trying. She must be the only severe patient of Dr. Jastreboff's who is square dancing in loud sound. It's difficult for her to concentrate on the instruction. Her esophagus problem is bad. Her eyes drip from conjunctivitis. Together with her tears, Carol's vision is clouded.

> Turn your partner round and round,
> till her feet are off the ground.
> Allemande left and do-si-do,
> to your partner, do a bow.
> Turn your partner with a fling.
> Promenade home and do a swing.
> Pass by and square through four,
> swing your partner round the floor!

Everything is so magnified. She shakes from fear, even though she loves the music, and she loves the steps. She is just so tired from hurting. She's afraid Fred will leave her if she doesn't keep dancing. *Why can't he realize what I'm trying so hard to do—to live!*

Carol also wonders whether she's dancing for the challenge of being in noise. She knows for sure it's for the satisfaction of faxing Dr. Jastreboff her accomplishments. "I made it! I'm square dancing in sound!" She sends the fax before she takes off her coat.

The next day, she conjures up an image of Dr. Jastreboff. He holds her fax in his hand. He goes around the clinic saying, "Look at this! Now my completely debilitated patient in San Francisco is square dancing!" Everyone applauds! Carol smiles at the thought. She smiles whenever she thinks of the Jastreboffs.

Carol calls Bethann in Los Angeles. She cries out to her best friend. "Tell me how I'm supposed to live through this thing. Fred can be so helpful sometimes. At the same time, he's so emotionally detrimental!"

"You know, Carol, your husband is never going to change. He's always been this way."

"Bethann, when I was well, I could cope with anyone and anything. Now I can't tolerate his lack of feeling. It's always business as usual with him. I don't know if there's anybody else in the world trying to live this way."

"I sure couldn't. I have a hard enough time doing the little that I do."

"The Jastreboffs think Fred is an angel from heaven. Dr. Jastreboff says to me, 'Don't be mad at your husband! He's still there! Most men would have left you long before now.'" Fred says, "At least a nice compliment from somebody!"

"Well, he is still there, Carol."

"I remember thinking, Bethann, when Dr. Jastreboff said that most men would have left, how rotten that would be for a woman who becomes critically ill. You take marriage vows for better or for worse. You're both healthy then, and who knows what life has in store for either one. This reminds me of something that I heard years ago. A woman told her husband that she had a disease that would eventually become apparent. She was okay at the time."

"So what did the husband do?"

"He left the next day!" Carol responds.

"Well, you do have to be thankful Fred is staying there. He brings in all your groceries. He's even cleaning house," Bethann reminds her.

"But it's just not enough to keep me going. Will you call Dr. Jastreboff and tell him how badly Fred behaves? I need his wisdom, any solutions he might have—either he or his wife. I have to live through this, Bethann. I want to, regardless of what I say and how torturous it is. I have to believe my parents and Charlie would be proud of me hanging onto my life.

"Please also ask if there is any chance the generators won't work? I need to know. I need you to be truthful with me. Okay? Promise?"

"I will, Carol. I'll call Dr. Jastreboff."

"Thanks, Bethann. I love you for trying to help."

Thirty minutes later, Bethann tells Carol, "I just talked to Dr. Margaret Jastreboff for quite a while."

"Dr. Margaret Jastreboff? What did she say?"

"Her husband is out of town for a few days. She'll have him call you when he returns. She said that with this condition, the spouse becomes the caretaker of the debilitated partner. The well spouse has more power than he or she ever had with the same person that they married. She said that in a couple of years, you would be back to your old self, functioning just like you used to. Then you can make your own decisions. You will again have all your choices of acting and speaking freely. She also said that oftentimes when the sick spouse recovers, the well one needs counseling."

"She said all that? Why?"

"Because with the return of good health, you might not agree to Fred's wishes so easily."

"That's true, Bethann. But with Fred, I really don't think that will be the case. He asks me before he does something. And besides, I know he'll jump for joy not having to grocery shop. He hates that. I'll take a lot of extra responsibilities off his shoulders.

"Did Dr. Jastreboff's wife really tell you all these things, Bethann? Will I be alive in two years? Is it possible that I will recover? It'll be like a dream come true!"

"Yes, she really did! You know, Carol, I was really impressed with this woman. She sounds wonderful, very intuitive and exceptionally intelligent!"

"You should know, Bethann, because that's how I think of you. I'm not kidding! I remember how you never even got a B all the way through UC Berkeley."

"I got a couple of B's," Bethann laughingly says, then adds, "Carol, you should be thankful your condition and suffering are happening in just a point of time. It's true, it's horrible beyond belief, but eventually it'll all be over. You'll be back to your usual giggly self. You probably will be helping everyone in the world with these problems. Then I'll say, 'That's my girlfriend from junior high!' "

"Ha! I'll trade my problems now with you," Carol kids.

"Do I get your figure, too?" Bethann jokes.

"I'd rather give you my ears," Carol responds, as she thanks her lifelong friend. She has survived another dreadful day!

All the king's horses and all the king's men
couldn't put Humpty together again.

213

Can anyone put all my broken pieces back? I want to try!
"Can I have my teeth repaired, Dr. Jastreboff?"

"Yes. You should take good care of your teeth and your body. Sometimes sound from dental work can temporarily increase tinnitus. You can turn up the generators a little during the drilling."

Carol goes to her local dentist for help. He is abrupt and unbending. "I can't work on your teeth. Your whole jaw has been shifted over."

"I'm trying to live through something painful. I can't survive unless I can eat. I can't eat with all my broken teeth." She tries to convince her longtime dentist to have a heart and change his mind. This dentist doesn't care that every tooth and filling in her mouth needs repair.

She recalls a very intelligent and personable young dentist who had done his apprenticeship under this one who now is unfeeling and refuses her as a patient. She telephones him at his own new practice. He's horrified to hear of her plight. "Of course I'll help you, Carol. We'll work around your medical condition. . . . Yes, I can replace crowns. We'll fix you up good as new."

Carol now has a dental hero. She works with him for months. She is eternally grateful for his skill and kindness. She cries because the sound of the drill is amplified. It's like an electric saw. She apologizes. He's understanding.

Other patients get instant relief from moving up the generator volume dial. This little trick forces the brain to listen to more sound. Thus, tinnitus becomes less important and quieter. For the average sufferer, higher volume means lower tinnitus. Unfortunately, at this stage in Carol's treatment, the increased volume makes her situation even more unbearable.

Her dentist salvages and restores every poor tooth in Carol's mouth. He even finds a severe abscess that requires surgery. Now she needs a surgeon.

Carol looks at the familiar oral surgeon she had gone to in the past. She recalls his surgery on the broken tooth from the oyster shell. Then afterwards, there were so many wrong treatments for her condition for such a horrible length of time. Too much unnecessary pain before finding Dr. Jastreboff.

The young surgeon's nurse is bewildered. "Why aren't you crying from all the injections into the roof of your mouth?"

"I'm used to pain!" she answers.

Dr. Gray, the ear surgeon with Dr. Jastreboff, calls numerous doctors, seeking medical help for Carol. She is grateful. When they hear about her condition from one of their colleagues, help will be on the way—she thinks. She is about to find out differently.

Carol sits in her new psychiatrist's office. *This one will help me live through the generator treatment, I hope.* He professes to understand all the drugs on the market. He does paperwork for her new HMO plan during her first session. He schedules a blood test during her second one.

Carol struggles to cross the street to the blood lab without passing out. Tears well up in her eyes in front of the technician. "Am I hurting your arm that much drawing blood?"

Should she try to explain that his footsteps are hurting her that much?

On the third visit, the psychiatrist issues an antipsychotic drug. "This is the latest thing used for multipurposes. It reduces fear. Try it!" She resents seeing the psychiatrist. *But if using another drug will save my life, I'll try.*

The seconds keep **tick, tick, ticking** away. The minutes turn to hours. And the hours become days. Carol prays for the strength to endure her pain! She swallows the medicine faithfully. *Do I really need this new drug or the psychiatrist?* Carol experiments. She stands next to her new refrigerator. She walks quickly through small stores. She drives short distances in her car. She forces herself to function in more and more kinds of sound.

She drives to Alameda. She sees a greeting card rack in the market across from Fred's office—It's Tobi! He made the front of a St. Patrick's Day card. It's a cocker spaniel, and he's adorable. He looks just like she imagines Tobi to be. She buys the card. She wears no headset in the store. She uses no ear protection. She stands defiantly in sound with just her generators. She is really proud of herself!

Chapter 31

Carol is back! She plays the board game for entertainment. Courage fights Fear. They are equally matched. Courage can grow stronger. Courage can surmount Fear. Courage can beat Fear. Courage works with the generators. She has to remove Fear from the board.

Nothing sounds normal in volume, yet Carol is here, out in the world again. Is this because of the time that she's been using the generators or the tablets she's swallowing? *I have to try next time without a drug. This will be the true test. I will do everything that Dr. Jastreboff suggests. I will never veer even an inch.*

Carol prays to be able to function normally in her home again, without terror. She wishes to walk on the street without fear. If she can reduce the anxiety and trauma, she'll live through more treatment time. The generators are kicking in. She believes in Dr. Jastreboff. His treatment will reverse all the hyperacusis. She goes home happy and hopeful. She has purchased an item in a store all by herself. She has used no ear protection. She uses only the generators as her treatment. She sends the happy news on her doggie card to the Jastreboffs—immediately, of course!

Carol's small radio plays music barely audible in the waiting room. She is now on her fourth psychiatric visit.

"Can you turn that music off!" the psychiatrist snaps. "I can't work in noise!"

Oh, really?

"Do I ever get to talk here?" *On television the patients lie on a couch and talk! He not only has no couch, he doesn't allow talking!*

"My only remedy for making my nonfunctional patients functional in our society is drugs. All mental states stem from chemical imbalances."

Oh, do they now? Not this one!

Carol gets up from the chair. She walks out of his office without a chemical imbalance. She does, though, have a very traumatized mental state. She doesn't want his help or his drugs. She walks away feeling a lot happier.

Carol starts to function again.

She still freaks out a lot. She still cries a lot. She is like a baby who has to learn to crawl before it can walk.

Regrettably, Dr. Gray's time on the phone with doctors has been wasted. Carol is sad and angry. Why can't she find a doctor who has the ability to understand these life-altering conditions? Dr. Jastreboff wants her to find a smart one! Aren't there any out there?

"I can't locate one!" Her voice bellows into Dr. Jastreboff's ear. "There just aren't any doctors smart enough to understand hyperacusis!"

Carol looks down at the name of the gastrointestinal referral. He is located in Berkeley. The distance—two cities away—seems like light years to travel.

"I'll take you to the stomach specialist you know in our town," Celia volunteers. Carol hesitates. He won't understand how it's possible to have a destroyed digestive tract, let alone an entire life!

Carol is in the office of the local stomach doctor with Celia. Carol asks him for help with what she should eat. "It doesn't

217

matter what you eat. I don't care if you eat s—t. Your emotions are the source of your problem." What kind of a doctor uses that kind of language to his patient? Not a very professional one! Carol and Celia walk out. Carol notices that Celia is carrying a large plant that had been decorating the doctor's office. The plant looks heavy, and the act of carrying it looks like theft.

"C-e-e-e-lia," Carol screams in horror. "Put that back! Two wrongs don't make a right!" A man wearing a business suit and carrying a briefcase walks toward them. Since they are in a medical complex, there is a good chance the man, whose face is buried in a newspaper, is a doctor.

"Celia, my sound tolerance doesn't include the noise of a prison, not quite yet!"

"I'm the one doing it," she replies.

"I'm already guilty by association, even though I'm innocent. They'll call me your accomplice."

"Oh, all right." Celia finally gives in and sets the plant down in the hallway.

"Aren't you going to put it back inside his office?"

"Nah. He doesn't deserve it. Let him have to look for it." Carol wants to insist, but she is really too sick and exhausted to protest further. Celia's crime is reduced from burglary to moving an object.

Celia is angry, like Carol, at the awful doctor's attitude, not to mention his uncouth language. "I didn't raise you to swear, Carol," her deceased mom lectures. Celia wakes Carol from her thoughts. "Don't you want something bad to happen to him, the way he acted?"

"Nothing that I can think of would be bad enough for him, unless . . . he could have to suffer from my medical condition."

Celia takes her to a farther-away stomach doctor. Carol listens to the recommended specialist in this medical group. "Your problem is not in my field. You need a psychiatrist!"

Again? What are they, in cahoots?

Carol will keep taking stomach medicine on her own. She will keep swallowing enough tranquilizers to stay alive on her own. She will keep fighting to recover, not on her own—she has Dr. Jastreboff and his family to help her, as well as her husband, her son, and her friends. She will keep seeking a gastrointestinal physician who is worthy of the title "doctor."

Carol and David go to the San Francisco Zoo. To her, it is a big deal. It's very obvious now that the generators are slowly reversing her condition. She watches the animals. She pretends the squeals from the monkeys are coming from oversized apes from a prehistoric time.

Her son buys her a rust-colored orangutan. Carol picks out a picture postcard of a gorilla. She writes on the card, "I now have a monkey in my house." Pretty soon, thanks to them, she won't have one on her back anymore. Carol describes the animal to the Jastreboffs. She needs to make sure they understand that "Rusty" is stuffed!

Time goes by. Carol is still alive. She even improves! Drs. Pawel and Margaret Jastreboff are making this possible. David makes this possible. Celia makes this possible. And even Fred makes this possible!

Dr. Jastreboff diligently returns her messages and faxes. She stays alive "for him." She wants to prove that her doctor's treatment works, so that no one else in the world will have to suffer as she has.

The generators are running, **rrrrrrr,** day and night. They reduce her stabbing ear pain. But she doubles over with replacement pain—esophagus refluxing. "Your brain is probably fried with sound by now," Dr. Jastreboff says sympathetically.

Like eggs, Carol thinks. She knows he understands the level of her suffering. His compassion never ceases to overwhelm her with tears of happiness. The empathy from his wife, as well, keeps adding to her strength and courage.

Carol needs to find immediate help for her refluxing from a nearby medical doctor. She keeps phoning her local internist who she thinks is sympathetic and understands her problems. He doesn't return her messages. She cannot endure the burning in her chest. The medicine isn't strong enough. She calls him again on a holiday. "This is an emergency. Please, I need help!"

She can't believe that it's her doctor on the phone. "What do you expect me to do? You probably always had stomach problems!" Carol cries and cries. She can't seem to get local medical assistance. She has no medical help across the bay in San Francisco either. Her only medical help comes from 3,000 miles away—from Baltimore, Maryland.

Carol wants to think that doctors take their oaths to help people, not humiliate them. But if her medical condition is not understood and believed, anything and everything the doctors try can be harmful. She vows to find an internist who is intelligent, and to find a gastrointestinal doctor whom she can respect. Then she will follow their instructions and get rid of her reflux problem.

Carol stands in front of her fax machine. "What's this?" She is feeling down in the dumps as she struggles against impossible odds. Suddenly, her odds seem to change. The incoming fax page has a picture of Tobi staring up at her. He looks just like the dog on the St. Patrick's Day card she had sent to the Jastreboffs. His bow is still tied around his neck. Attached is his four-leaf clover, which reads, "Just for You." Tears well up in her eyes as she studies Dr. Jastreboff's note at the bottom of the page:

April 16, 1996:
I am happy that you are getting so much better! Keep working on your tinnitus and hyperacusis! Pawel J. Jastreboff.

Carol looks at the clock—**tick tick tick tick.** It is no longer her enemy. It speaks out late into the night. She thinks that Dr.

Margaret Jastreboff had a hand in cloning Tobi through her fax machine. She smiles at the thought. She notices an apparent loudness drop-off in external sounds. She walks into her kitchen. She sits under the fluorescent light buzz. Everything is still annoying, but she can stand it.

She and Celia walk down the street. Carol carries her headset for security. She stays right next to her good friend for safety. Celia stops to talk to a neighbor. The man is sitting in his car letting the engine idle. Carol stands close by. The running engine hasn't killed her. She sits down on the street curb. She's really out in sound now. She is making her debut back into the world. No one can comprehend her small feats, her condition, her extreme fear, no one except Dr. Jastreboff. She's still afraid of all creatures of noise—birds, trees, dogs, cats, people's voices, cars, planes, everything. Carol needs Celia to walk her home, clear to the front door of her house.

Now Carol's thoughts turn to revenge. She blames the doctors. Which ones were the worst? They all were!

Carol's misguided journey began at home, with her husband. He listened to and followed uninformed doctors' advice. He thought they knew what they were talking about. It was too bad for her that they didn't—and still don't!

She shares her anger and feelings of frustration with Dr. Jastreboff. He replies, "Fighting only makes sense if you have a chance of winning. Put your energy toward good things. Do positive things. There is nothing more rewarding than helping others."

Her doctor is a humanitarian. He tries to replace her vindictiveness with goals for the future—her future—by telephone, by fax, and by computer from Baltimore.

"I'll try to get rid of my hate and anger," she promises him. *Will I ever?* Fred suggests that she write a book about her recent experiences. *A real book with a cover?*

"It'll be good therapy for you," he says.

Dr. Jastreboff adds his advice. "Show contrasts of how you were before, compared to now." *I was alive before. Now I'm rising from the dead!*

Fred makes it official. He brings home a computer and monitor. Noises from the equipment frighten her. "I'll teach you how to use it. It'll take hours of hard work and patience for us both, but we can do it!" Fred is persistent and says, "It'll be wonderful habituation!"

Carol tells Dr. Jastreboff, "Doctors need to hear my story."

He corrects her. "People need your story."

She uses the howling computer. She writes exactly the truth. Fred reads her work. He leaves a note written on her paperwork next to the piece about his square dancing do-si-dos. It says, "This is really overdone. I get you out of the house to do something enjoyable, and you give me no credit or the slightest sign of appreciation." *I do now!*

Carol complains to the Jastreboffs. "Fred doesn't want me to write my story the way it actually happened."

"Just write the truth," Dr. Pawel Jastreboff tells her.

"There are always two sides to a story," Dr. Margaret Jastreboff says. Carol agrees with them both. So she writes down everything everyone said so there'll be no hard feelings. Carol's book will follow Dr. Jastreboff around the world. He gives courses for professionals and lectures throughout the United States and in Europe. He speaks five languages. She brags to everyone she comes in contact with, "My doctor is so smart, you know. He saved my life!"

She even writes to tell William Shatner the same thing. The *Star Trek* celebrity kindly responds, "I share your high opinion of Dr. Jastreboff. He's helped me considerably."

Carol gets panic attacks when she knows the Jastreboffs are going to be away. They hop to Europe almost as often as Fred has to go to the grocery store to shop for her.

She remembers, and she types. Every word is written with suffering, pain, and tears. She thinks about the disturbing computer noise in the same way as she previously thought of her generators, like a motor boat. She stops complaining about the generators. They quiet down simultaneously with the outside noise reduction. The gain in her auditory system decreases. She recalls every word Dr. Jastreboff has said.

"You will get well! You will recover! I would like to get you back on the ski slopes. I would like to put you in front of the cameras to tell your story." She can only visualize Dr. Jastreboff's wishes in a "hyperacusic" fashion. How far away and impossible they seem. . . .

Carol pictures herself on a ski slope. She shudders from the noise her skis make. The skiers increase the volume level by dropping their equipment into the outside compartment of the tram. The sounds copy firecrackers exploding. The squeaks from the chairs and cables screech like chains scraping on railroad tracks.

She skis to the bottom of the run. She feels like she has to use the bathroom right away. She shakes the frozen ice off and unsnaps her bindings. She digs her skis and poles into the snow. She ascends the slippery steps of the warm-up facility.

Deafening noise hits her ears. The room is not crowded. A few people are eating. "Make this stop happening!" she screams. "It can't be real! It must be a bad dream." She wants to run. She wants to escape. The bathroom door slams with a thunderous clap.

The women run water in the basins. They smile as they look into the mirror. They laugh and talk. Some stomp their heavy ski boots to remove snow. The boots bang into the cement tile with tons of force.

Carol still needs to use the bathroom. How can she? "Won't someone please tell me how?"

N*ow she imagines herself in front of the cameras to talk about tinnitus and hyperacusis. The talk show host says, "We have a person here today to explain conditions of suffering that affect over two hundred and fifty million people throughout the world."*

Carol sits on a chair. She looks normal. The cameras roll as she watches the interviewer's lips move. The voice of the host sounds unreal. The microphone is plugged into too many amplifiers. The sounds are too intense!

The audience is rude! They seem to be stomping around the room like a stampede of wild horses. The applause sounds like cymbals clanging in response. Why can't they just clap quietly with their hands?

Yes, yes. I will stay on the mountain. I won't be afraid of a bathroom! I'll talk in front of a camera. I'll show Dr. Jastreboff that I can do good things. I want him to know that all his efforts to save my life have been well spent. I need him to be proud of me. But I can't do all of this yet! She snaps back to the present.

Carol phones her doctor. "Be patient," he says. "Keep going with the generators."

Dr. Jastreboff gives Carol his knowledge and treatment. She follows his protocol. His feelings, time, and caring gradually bring back her courage and strength. She utilizes all her hobbies and interests as much as she is able. She works hard for a very long time to get well. This is the recipe that will completely reverse her hyperacusis first and then alleviate her perception of the tinnitus.

Chapter 32

People jog and walk to lose weight. Not Carol. She bikes to use sound. She is the only person on the popular marina by the bay who exercises for this reason. She is the only one in the entire State of California who exercises, not for a healthy body and heart, but for healthy ears. She does not know if her shattered spirit will ever heal. But she sure tries to mend her auditory system.

Carol counts the number of miles she pedals each day. She continually walks and bikes. When she gets tired, she walks and bikes some more. She visits her neighborhood branch library often. It is her destination point for a walk in sound. The stacks of books she lugs home are the means by which she refocuses her attention. This allows the generators to work faster.

She also walks just for diversion, alone, after dark. She knows that this is not safe, but what's worse, being mugged or living with horrible magnification of sound?

"Hyperacusis wins," her little game says. It is more frightening and bloodcurdling than anything else in the world. One who experiences the terrors of hyperacusis is guaranteed, assuming he stays alive, to never have any worse fears. Everything else will be diminished.

Carol's longtime fear of flying has disappeared. Now she even looks fondly at bugs which she used to fear and hate. She no longer is afraid of anything but the hyperacusis.

"Use your craft work to divert your attention," Dr. Margaret Jastreboff suggests. Carol adores knitting. She now knits to recover. She bikes down to the waterfront. Her knitting bag hangs from the handlebars. She sits next to the surf as it crashes onto the rocks. And she knits. She shudders from the planes in the sky. She cringes from all the other obtrusive sounds. But all the little noises gradually become just what they are, little and unimportant.

She turns on the television, very low at first. She has not seen the news for almost three years. She has not watched her favorite soap opera or any movies during this time. Her soap has not changed. Everything else has!

She quickly reaches outside the patio for her *Oakland Tribune*. She revels in her small abilities. *What? The paper looks different. The format is altered!*

Her local streets have been remodeled. Stores have gone out of business. New ones have opened. Her head starts to spin. She cries as she looks. She realizes all the infinitesimal things she has missed for so long.

She buys a half dozen small inexpensive radios, like her favorite one. She uses them for sound throughout her house. Since they are water resistant, she puts them in the bathrooms, too. Her radios are wonderful. They work along with the generators to bring her back into the world she once knew.

She tries to attend the square dancing classes. Each session is a conditioning for sound. She wants to please her husband by continuing, even though she still isn't ready. Most of all, she wants to please her wonderful doctor back East through her efforts and progress.

"Will you take me to the motor movies?" Carol asks Fred.

"Sure, if you think you can stand the noise."

At the drive-in, Fred starts to get up. Carol screams, "Don't leave me alone in the car!"

"I'll be right back. I have to go to the restroom!"

Carol shakes with fear. She gets out of the car. She stands in the middle of the drive-in parking lot seeking solace. While waiting for Fred to come back, she looks up at the moon.

"Who knew that there were more noises at night to frighten me?" she asks the face on the beautiful moon that stares back at her. The face answers her question.

"You, Dr. Jastreboff, and other severely affected sufferers."

If I told someone that my auditory system picks up electrical vibrations, what would he think, dear moon? I remember when I once did tell someone. "Fred, I hear the current from the wires outside, honest I do. . . ." It was such a very long time ago . . . I was not listened to . . . I was not believed . . . I had known it would be like this . . . but I didn't know it would stay like this. Nothing has changed in this medical field since then. . . .

"They all think you are crazy, absolutely crazy!" the intelligent moon responds.

I have to have an effect on all this disbelief! I have to be Dr. Jastreboff's proof. Carol sobs as she places her head down on the roof of the car. *I can and I will!* she keeps repeating to herself.

Fred returns. He looks at his wife. "Are you okay?"

"Oh, yes." *I just had a nice conversation with the moon.*

"Do you want to try a movie in a regular theater, Mom?"

"I can't, David. At least in the drive-in, I can control the volume. It's wonderful being able to watch television and movies again, but I have to take it slowly."

"But Mom, the film I had in mind for you to try is animated. It won't be in THX sound. It'll be quieter."

"What's THX, David?"

"THX and digital sound have come out while you've. . . ."

Carol finishes her son's sentence, "While I've been busy dying, right?"

"You're going to make it, Mom!"

"With a son like you, how can I not? What's the name of this picture, David?"

"*Oliver.* You love dogs so much. I think you'll love this film!"

"Well, I love you, that's for sure."

"Love you, too, Mom."

Carol and David go to the theater. She looks at the theater stub as tears roll down her face. She watches her son standing in the popcorn line. She still feels like a member of an unknown species from another planet. But the planet she's on is slowly approaching earth again.

She loves *Oliver.* She tolerates the volume level just fine. She becomes more confident. "Let me try the film next door, David, the one with Richard Gere."

"Are you sure, Mom?"

"Yes," she says daringly, as they walk into the adjoining theater. Carol breaks into a sweat. She reaches for her headset and puts it on. "I need to leave, David. I'm going to pass out. It's so loud!"

"Are you okay now?" David asks.

Carol composes herself in the lobby. "Yes. I'm all right. I guess it was a little too much, a little too soon. I'm thankful for the movie I did see. I'm thankful just to be alive! I'll be patient and keep going with the generators."

At home, she puts the movie stub in an envelope and addresses it to Drs. Pawel and Margaret Jastreboff. She wants them to have a little souvenir from her latest brave undertaking in the San Francisco Bay Area.

Carol used to unconsciously study the fashion ensembles worn by people walking in the street. Before she realized what she was doing, she had analyzed everyone's choice of style and color within view.

Now she automatically calculates decibels of power emissions every place she goes. She compares this activity with the one she had engaged in when she was in the fashion industry. Instead of reviewing fashions, she critiques sound and power sources before she moves an inch. She doesn't want to do this. It's a safety mechanism, a shield against pain, and a means of finding a safe zone.

With hyperacusis ruling her every move, she cautiously is beginning to function again. Her actions are being viewed by others as peculiar, but she is so very thankful to be returning to some normal tasks and activities that it doesn't really matter what they think.

A psychiatrist not understanding Dr. Jastreboff's profession and methods would undoubtedly describe a patient like Carol as "emotionally disturbed." Her emotions are indeed disturbed. Whose wouldn't be? She realizes that she is deeply traumatized. She still needs more help. She wants to visit the Jastreboffs again. She hasn't seen them for almost eight months. It's time she was tested again. She wants to see how much progress she has made from wearing the generators and from following Dr. Jastreboff's protocol to the letter.

"Please Fred, take me to see Dr. Jastreboff. I need to find out how to function again." Carol still has a way to go.

Fred and Carol are flying to Baltimore for a second testing. She needs Dr. Jastreboff's counseling. She wants to reverse the trauma like the generators are reversing her hyperacusis.

Fred makes wonderful travel plans. Carol's seat is in the quiet front of the plane. The volume level seems okay. Could everything possibly be at a normal sound level?

Carol is so excited! Soon she's going to be able to see the Jastreboffs again. She views her trip as a fun excursion. She always thinks of them like the family she desperately needs.

She chats in Spanish with the couple in the next seat. She discovers that they own a business in her town, and that they are getting off in Las Vegas, her stopover point. Their enjoyment is from gambling. Her enjoyment is from being able to sit on the plane, in sound, without total panic.

Carol watches the passengers move down the aisle to disembark. She waits for Fred who sits in the last row on the plane because of his high-pitched hyperacusis. How many people on this plane would believe her story?

"I didn't even need the headset, Fred. The plane engine sounded loud, but fine! It even drowned out the sound of my generators. The droning of the motors gave me temporary comfort from the horrible tinnitus. Isn't that great?"

"That sure is! Come on. We have to run if we're going to catch our connecting flight. I think we have time to use the restrooms, but unfortunately we can't stop to look around. Las Vegas has really changed since the last time we were here. Maybe on the way back, we can take a look."

She hesitates. "Fred, will you wait right here for me?" She points to a specific spot for him to wait. "I'll only be a minute in the bathroom. You won't start walking away without me, will you?" She looks at the bathroom with trepidation.

"I'll stay right here."

Carol takes a deep breath and enters the "lions' den." She looks at the sparkling clean basins with their automatic faucets. She realizes that she doesn't even know how to turn on the water. It seems that she has forgotten how to do the simplest things.

She looks at her formerly off-limit products. The paper towels look harmless enough. The soap container no longer is bad. *I was so brainwashed before—it was as deep as my traumatized state is now. I have to keep talking to myself. I'm beyond all this. All those things were nonsense, just wished-for panaceas. Of course I can touch colored paper towels, soap, unfiltered water—anything I want to. This is in my ears, not in my mind or body. I dare anyone in the world to tell me different!*

She purposely grabs a colored paper towel and vigorously dries her hands with it. She unconsciously turns her hands over. She looks for the color dye stains. Of course . . . they aren't there!

Chapter 33

In Baltimore, Carol recalls the street where the Inner Harbor Marriott stands. The buildings are mostly brick. She remembers the driveway and the entrance to the hotel, but everything else comes up blank. She sees the area where she and Fred had sat with Dr. Jastreboff. She stares at the escalator. How noisy it seemed the last time. It doesn't appear quite as alarming today.

She looks around the hotel room. She can't recall the furnishings from the previous visit eight months ago. All that registers are her memories of pain and her thoughts of suicide and death.

"Carol, can you please fill up the ice bucket? I'd really appreciate it."

Another test! She hesitates. Her mental conditioning makes her analyze the menial task that looms so heavily ahead. *Should I attempt to satisfy Fred's request?* She starts to calculate: *Just walk down the hallway. The air conditioning will run through the vents. There're hallway lights, and then the monster ice contraption. It's only a machine. How loud can ice cubes resound? Could be pretty loud!* She shudders. She decides to chance it and takes the bucket from Fred.

"Okay, but I'll only be seeing if I can. I'm not promising." She wants to be sure that this is clear to Fred. *He seems so relaxed and patient. He acts so differently than during our last visit. I needed so much help then. Maybe I don't need so much now. Tomorrow's testing will answer my questions. What does Dr. Jastreboff think about me? He knows I'm much better. I'm acting nicer and crying a lot less.*

Carol counts the ice cubes one by one as they fall into the bucket. She doesn't cry or run. She watches and listens to the silly ice machine just like a child would. She has been reborn. The satisfaction and pride she feels equate to that of a new mother's joy. She is really proud of herself. Carol decides to take only one tranquilizer at bedtime. She is "gutting out" her condition on her own strength.

Hyperacusis extracts all feelings of self-worth. It humiliates its victims and strips them of normal feelings and actions. Carol is conquering the enemy!

"**H**i, Karen!" Carol warmly greets Dr. Jastreboff's audiologist. Carol knows the routine. She grips the button, ready to hear the first frequency. This is her test. Very soon Dr. Jastreboff will be scoring her answers. She is excited. She is well prepared today.

It's absolutely ridiculous for others to be nervous about this painless, simple testing. She has a much larger goal to achieve: victory over her total fear of the world she once lived in.

She consciously counts the increased volume of tones that come through her headset. The sounds start out low. Every additional one is just a little louder. She counts eight levels. *Hmmm . . . that's interesting.* She counts exactly eight tones that are fine in the other ear, too. She wonders whether she is deliberately letting the volume go up eight times to match what the first ear tolerated.

Why am I such a precision nut? Fred is the CPA. He needs to get his numbers to match, not me. Yet I know I just did this with my sound testing. I could have pushed the button on the seventh tone. But then the other ear listened to eight tones, so I didn't want to. Could this have something to do with wanting to be so exact on my knitting?

After finishing, she says, "I'm going back to the hotel room, Fred, while you're in the testing. I'm just going to run down the street and race into the elevator. I'll just try to pretend that I'm not freaking out. Bye!"

Fred gives his wife a kiss. "Good luck!"

"Wait!" Randie says, as she starts to leave. "Dr. Jastreboff wants you to come back this afternoon. He wants you to have an additional test."

"Okay." Once again Carol is touched by the caring of her brilliant and conscientious doctor. She closes her eyes. She tries not to analyze the sound emissions in the elevator as it slowly descends. She races to the front door of the medical building and dashes through it without looking.

"Oops, all my things. . . ." Carol looks up at the man she has just collided with.

"I'll help you!" he says kindly.

"I'm so sorry! I'm really sick. I need to get off the street, quickly!"

The man gives her a funny look. *Should I explain?* She watches him as he goes about retrieving the important papers she has brought for Dr. Jastreboff.

Carol has not seen her doctor yet. Soon she will. She can't wait to see the Jastreboffs and show them her writing, which at this moment is blowing all over the sidewalk.

"I came clear across the United States," she explains, "to see my wonderful doctor in this building." The man runs furiously up and down, fighting the wind, trying his best to collect the escaping pages.

"So did I," he responds breathlessly.

"You did?" She looks for generators around his ears.

Carol thinks everyone in the clinic wears instruments in their ears. She assumes everyone in the waiting room of the ear department is here only for Dr. Jastreboff's Hyperacusis and Tinnitus Center. In fact, she figures everyone entering or exiting the medical building is a patient of Dr. Jastreboff. She wants the whole United States to become famous for her doctor and his treatment. *This will happen. You'll see!*

She gradually starts to realize that there are many doctors in many other specialties in "her" brick building on the corner. She now hears about one, as she listens to the collision man.

"Yes, my doctor is the finest gastroenterologist there is."

Carol's still-keen hearing grabs hold of the specialty the stranger's doctor practices. *That's who I need. I'll keep him in mind for future reference. If I live, that is. . . .*

The man retrieves Carol's smudged papers and hands them to her. She thanks him. They say good-bye. She turns around and starts to run again, even faster than before, back toward the hotel.

*W*hat's this? On her last trip, she hadn't noticed a gift shop. It's located right next to the lounge area where she and Fred had sat with Dr. Jastreboff.

I'd love to go in there. Will I die if I do? I'll stay only a minute. Besides, that cute young employee in the store has a really good cut of the same hairstyle I'm wearing.

Carol wears her hair exceptionally short. It resembles the younger generation's punk rock styles. Young people cut their hair that way for the "look." Carol cuts it for hyperacusis. Her showers that reverberate like Niagara Falls make short hair a necessity, not a choice.

"Where did you get your hair done?" she asks the adorable young woman.

"Do you really like it?" the girl working the gift shop replies, so pleased.

"You would probably look cute with *no* hair," Carol tells her.

She forgets her one-minute restriction and her hyperacusis. She chats with the girl. A man who is carrying boxes of baseball supplies enters. He obviously owns a souvenir business. "I see you have the Orioles well in stock," Carol comments.

"Oh, yes. We have a great team!"

"I know you do! You have a lot of great things. You have my doctor here in Baltimore. He's the most wonderful man in the world!" Carol has to let him know.

"Yes. We have some pretty good ones, that we do!"

"I went to the same high school as one of your famous baseball players who lives in Maryland. He's in the Hall of Fame. Do you know Ron Hansen?"

The man looks up, very surprised. "Oh? Of course I know him. Well, I don't really know him, but everyone in these parts knows of him!"

Carol smiles and lets out a short laugh. The man thinks she's proud of herself for being at the same high school as their Maryland hero. She's happy just to be standing in sound long enough to talk about baseball.

Ron Hansen is famous for his unassisted triple play. Carol wants Dr. Jastreboff, with his scientific medical breakthrough, to be in the Hall of Fame, too. He has already contributed so much to humankind. He's saving lives all over the world. He is so deserving. Soon his name will be connected with sound just as Ron Hansen's name is connected to baseball.

A baseball game. Hmmm. . . . Not many places can produce more sound than a packed stadium. Attending an Orioles game would be a significant accomplishment for me. I feel it! I will walk into a baseball stadium. I will measure the thunderous roar of thousands of people there. I'll be nervous and I'll be scared, but I'm going to do it! As sure as my name is Carol, I know this will happen one day.

Back in her room, she is absolutely thrilled that she had been able to chat for a while in the gift shop. She sure misses talking to no end! She looks down at the deep red ceramic crab with the eyes that jiggle that she has just bought. She places her gift on the table next to the phone. The crab's feet have tiny claws. He's cute! He's a magnet that says, "Baltimore, MD." Carol buys this for her refrigerator, the one she used to fear not so very long ago.

Suddenly, she's startled by the phone. Before she has a chance to wonder who would be calling, she hears, "I nearly fell off my chair reading your test results! Your hyperacusis is completely gone! You registered off my machinery!" Dr. Jastreboff says excitedly.

Tears fall onto her small magnet. She struggles to keep from sobbing. She hears so much happiness in the voice of her doctor. He is full of hope for the future, *her* future!

"There *can* be a future for you," she recalls hearing him say so long ago. "You *can* have a normal life!"

At this moment in Baltimore, she makes a vow: *I will never, ever think about suicide again. I will never let Dr. Jastreboff down, not after all his hard work with me for such a long time!*

"Hooray!" She jumps up and down all over the hotel room. She tosses her slippers up into the air like a baseball. She sits down. She wipes away the tears of joy. *I can actually go into as much sound as I want! But wait! How do you get over shell shock?*

Chapter 34

Tonight, Carol's eyes won't stop tearing. Tonight, Carol is in a beautiful Baltimore restaurant. Tomorrow, she will see Drs. Pawel and Margaret Jastreboff again. She can hardly wait. She watches Fred eat and drink. It still hurts to swallow. She prays that someday this, too, will be better, just like her hyperacusis.

Only one other couple is still in the restaurant. While waiting for their taxi, Carol and Fred chat with the two friendly Baltimorians who offer a tour of the city plus a ride back to the Marriott. She and Fred accept their magnanimous offer and cancel a taxicab. Carol thinks back for a moment about how everything started . . . about the other taxi—the one in Bermuda.

The couple believes her sad story. There are still some kind people in the world. She hopes to find a kind internist and an understanding gastrointestinal doctor back home. Her perspective is changing, like her hyperacusis. She and Fred thank the couple who have taken the time to show them around. Carol says, "I won't forget your kindness." The happy couple celebrate their wedding anniversary. Carol celebrates her return to the human race!

The next day, Dr. Jastreboff still sounds thrilled. "You registered off my equipment," he repeats.

Carol is in a daze. She hadn't been able to tolerate the air or the wind before. Now she wants to know, "Is my nonfunctional crisis over? Finished? Done with?"

Dr. Jastreboff responds, "Go out into the world and start enjoying life again. Go to Hawaii!"

Hawaii? A vacation? "But what about that other test you had me take? Karen says it's an auditory brain stem response. Is my brain fine?" Dr. Jastreboff laughs. *Did I make a joke?*

"Everything is normal!"

She still feels far from normal. "You know what I did? I made an appointment to have an 'Esophagogastroduodenoscopy'"— she struggles to read the procedure correctly from her notebook papers—"almost the minute the plane lands when we get home. What good is my recovery if I don't have a digestive tract? It's still really bad and I'm trying to eat and I'm taking all these stomach pills."

"I have my own remedy, a mixture of herbs which are soothing. If you'd like to try some . . . ?" Dr. Jastreboff offers.

"Yes, yes!"

Carol's opinion coincides with Dr. Jastreboff's. Had she been able to find him in the beginning of her problem, her digestive tract would still be intact. The doctors had done horrible things to her. She had kept pleading continually for treatments, anything to try to get relief.

"The other day I had a patient who had even taken electric shock treatments," Dr. Jastreboff sadly reports, shaking his head.

"The internist I'm using now wanted me to take those. Thank God, I didn't listen to him. Can you imagine?"

She is happy Dr. Jastreboff agrees with her viewpoints regarding everything awful connected with her afflictions. The lengths his sick patients go to in order to save their lives saddens him. She hears her own anger and frustrations echoed in his sentiments.

"Have the hospital call me as soon as they finish your surgical procedure. I want to know the results."

"Okay, I'll tell them. I'm so scared that they'll find something permanently damaged."

"I think it'll be okay. Why don't we take a break and then we can talk some more."

"Sounds good to me," Fred says to Carol. "Let's go up to the Lexington Market and look around."

She feigns a smile. *Which is stronger, Courage or Trauma? "Pick a card," an inner voice dares her.*

This market is much more than a grocery store. It is a food pavilion like those she's seen in foreign countries. It looms large and threatening as they approach.

"Boy, am I hungry!"

Boy, am I afraid! Carol doesn't reply. Instead, she walks on the sidewalk, shaking. They enter the market. Her ears have been closed off from sound for three years. *You can do it!*

Fred watches the food being prepared behind the counters. *How am I supposed to boldly walk back into the world?* She stands quivering in the noisy market. *What do you expect? You want Dr. Jastreboff to take you by the hand and help you function? Yes! Is that so bad?*

The market is unique. There is nothing like it in the San Francisco area. She views everything differently now. She is grateful and appreciative to see even the smallest objects, things that once seemed so unimportant to her.

She feels disoriented. She feels awkward. She wants to be strong, to make decisions, and to be able to function alone again. *I can't!*

"Please stay right next to me, Fred. Don't leave me by myself in here!"

"I won't!"

Oh, good! He's switched to his caring self again. Who could possibly understand Fred, let alone hyperacusis?

Back in the medical office, Dr. Jastreboff explains to Fred, "Your wife no longer has hyperacusis, but you still do!"

239

Did I wish it on him?

"What is the difference between our conditions?" Fred wants to know.

Carol feels angry. She speaks immediately. "Yours is specific sound frequencies and mine *was* clear across the board."

How can he possibly ask that? For years he has washed the dishes and clothes, cleaned, and shopped. He has witnessed and listened to my screams, tortured outbursts, and threats of suicide to end my misery. Yet he has to ask such a question!

Millions of people are able to live with the level of Fred's problem. They manage to function. They may not be enjoying their lives, but they are forced to do this simply because they don't know that Dr. Jastreboff can help them overcome their auditory problems.

Dr. Jastreboff previously explained to us the difference between specific sound frequency hyperacusis and total debilitation from the affliction. Fred looks amazed. Now he expects me to function like the person he married. Now he's going to say, "I'm the one with the hyperacusis."

"You'll just have to wear the generators a few months longer," Dr. Jastreboff tells Fred.

Carol's long-ago wish has come true. She kneels to wrap her arms around the beautiful tan cocker spaniel. "You are so cute, Tobi. You're indeed a little sweetheart." Tobi wags his tail in understanding. "Yes, you know I love dogs, don't you?" The animal watches everyone.

She doesn't want to leave Baltimore. She feels safe near the Jastreboffs. *I won't make it without you both!* She still has the horrendously severe tinnitus to overcome. And she still doesn't know how to cope with it.

She pets Tobi. She is so thankful to be alive. Her feelings of love and connection to the Jastreboffs are strong. She will always want to be a part of their lives. She hopes that they will want her to be. Her attention suddenly shifts from Tobi to Dr. Jastreboff's shocking words.

"Some of the victims in the Oklahoma bombing already have auditory symptoms of hyperacusis. I read their statistics. I can tell you how you can get hyperacusis back again."

Dr. Jastreboff's looking straight at me. No, I don't want to hear! I don't want to know! Carol puts her hands over her generators and shakes her head and says out loud, "No!" *This is horrible! Who knows besides Dr. Jastreboff? Nobody will understand it! Down the line, some innocent victim will commit suicide. The family will say, "He never bounced back mentally from what happened to him." Oh, my God! My story needs to reach both prosecutors and defense attorneys fast, really fast!*

It's too late! She hears Dr. Jastreboff's words that scare her even more. "If you're in a place where a pipe bomb goes off, this can cause hyperacusis."

Carol gets goosebumps thinking of her friend, Ruth Rasor. "The air bags exploding, too, right?" Dr. Jastreboff nods in agreement. "No one knows these things?" she asks for confirmation. Dr. Jastreboff again shakes his head to agree with Carol.

Her mind shifts to types of accidents while Fred and Dr. Jastreboff are conversing. Airline disasters, heavy-car impact crashes, explosions, air bags, gunshots. If you live through something horrendous like Carol's crash in the taxi—*"We're going to die!" Fernando's cry never leaves her memory*—you'll wish to God you hadn't.

People who routinely work in heavy noise should definitely use some sort of ear protection. Young people should protect their ears from loud concerts and blasting music as a preventive for what she struggles to live through. Carol pulls out a tissue and dabs at her tears.

A short while later, the conversation still encompasses the horrors of tinnitus and hyperacusis. The setting has changed, though, as Carol leans back to rest comfortably in Dr. Jastreboff's car. She listens to Fred and Dr. Jastreboff. She is tired, so terribly tired. . . .

"I must have caught my problems from Carol," Fred seriously says, as if it could be communicable!

She can't believe what her husband is saying, and to her brilliant doctor yet. The very nerve!

Carol recalls how Fred had fallen asleep at the wheel of his car years ago. He had been doing tax returns for two and a half days straight without sleep through April 15. She remembers the $3,000 the city wanted for the utility pole he knocked down. He was lucky to have survived!

It doesn't matter how you get these afflictions. What's important is that you know whom to go to for the correct treatment. Carol yawns. The movement of the car is making her sleepy.

"I think you got your condition from an alien," Dr. Jastreboff jokingly tells Fred.

Yea! That's my doctor!

Fred makes no response. Carol thinks Fred is flabbergasted. Dr. Jastreboff's comment is precious! She giggles.

Carol strains to keep her eyes open. She is exhausted and feels so weary from her lengthy battle with everything and everyone. She falls asleep. She starts to dream. . . .

"Not guilty!" the judge says. "You did not give your husband tinnitus and hyperacusis. All you others out there who claim to know what causes these afflictions and how to treat them, speak now or forever hold your peace!" The black-robed man bangs his gavel for attention in the courtroom. He begins his dissertation.

"Wear your seat belts and don't drive when you drink! Don't ride in cars with air bags! Don't abuse your ears with loud music, and if you work in high-noise environments, please wear ear protection! In other words, take care of your ears like you do your other body parts. Then you may never know the horrors of tinnitus and hyperacusis. Know now that we finally have a treatment that alleviates the pain and suffering from these conditions. We have a neuroscientist who discovered a cure. Does anyone here dispute what I have said?"

The judge looks at Carol, who timidly raises her hand.

"Speak up, Woman, You who stand before me and dare to question what I say!" The judge is angry.

Carol's voice is shaky as she starts to speak. She glances at the important paperwork she has carried so far.

"Your Honor. . . ." She clears her throat. "My condition is something you should know about. My new sunglasses started

everything. I bought them the week before I had my eye problems. They were sprayed, sprayed with awful chemicals. Then I dipped myself into more chemicals with a chemically unbalanced swimming pool. This mixed into the leaking gasoline fumes I inhaled from the stove where I stayed in Mexico. All of this tremendous amount of poison got into my eyes and seeped through my head and then flowed into my ears. If it didn't all get into my ears automatically, the bug that flew into my ear pushed the rest of the toxins in—that's when I was on my bicycle, the bug, I mean. I bike ride, you know." She feels a lump in her throat. She needs to continue despite her reflux problem.

"I deserve to be punished right here in your courtroom. I was vain. I put poison into my body by using color dye on my hair. I wasn't even satisfied with that horrible sin. I added more bad solutions to make my colored hair curly."

She looks up at the judge to see if he is still listening. Gee. . . . He's leaning so far over his stand to look at me, his eyeglasses are going to slip off!

The judge thinks, This Woman is never going to stop talking!

"Your Honor, I didn't stay home to clean my house. I left my poor dog unattended for selfish motives. I wanted to swim. I wanted to have fun. I shirked my responsibilities instead of doing my chores."

"Nonsense, Woman! All that is rubbish!"

"But Your Honor, people like me don't believe that these generators retrain your auditory system. How can you retrain something that you cannot see? Where is the proof of this claim? Tell me! Explain it, can you?"

"Hmmm." I should hang her right now. "A very intelligent question, My Dear!"

Carol is so happy. She is back in the good graces of the powerful judge. Her status has risen from a commoner with "garbagey evidence" to one capable of an intelligent question.

She and Fred had read Dr. Jastreboff's information in the American Tinnitus Association's quarterly journal when she first became sick. Fred had said, "Do you want to wear things in your ears like some people are doing?"

"No!" she had answered, sobbing. "There is no way I can lis-ten to more noise!" Her thoughts are directed back to the judge in the robe.

"The brain focuses in on the sound from the constant gener-ator noise. Through consistent use of the generators and consid-erable time, no other sounds become important to the brain. This includes tinnitus," the judge informs her. "Think of tinnitus as something being picked up and tossed aside. It is being given no importance and no significance by your brain. Your brain tells your auditory system, 'You just simply do not matter anymore, tinnitus. I have my generator noises with me to be my friends.' Does everyone in this courtroom understand?" the judge wants to know. But the judge glares only at Carol. He bangs his gavel. There is silence in the courtroom.

He continues: "This really isn't that complicated. When something is not that important anymore, its significance reduces down and down—to a total nothing. This is what the generators do to tinnitus. The volume level of those intrusive, horrible noises drops and drops and drops. Eventually, these sounds will not annoy you or bother you. When you are able to completely ignore tinnitus, you have completely habituated it. In fact, the process is called 'The Habituation of Tinnitus.' Many patients do not hear tinnitus at all anymore. Then you can say good-bye to your gener-ator friends. You will not need to wear them."

"Is the brain really that powerful to be able to completely retrain our auditory systems?" Carol asks the judge. She doesn't mean to challenge him.

"Of course it is! Don't you realize that your brain is respon-sible for all your emotions, even your constant sobbing, Mrs. Brook?" (Sobbing—that is so obnoxious, like You, Woman!)

The knowledgeable judge addresses her and the others in the court who are now all listening attentively. "Our brain controls our limbic system. If it can do that, then why can't it be in charge of our auditory system?"

The judge dares anyone to refute his words. No one does. Not even Carol.

Chapter 35

Carol opens her eyes. Dr. Jastreboff is still behind the wheel of his car. He and Fred have been talking. She remembers laughing when Dr. Jastreboff joked about the alien. Also, she has a vague recollection that some humor involved someone wearing a long dress carrying a hatchet.

She knows she has just visited with the Jastreboffs and Tobi. That was real for sure! But the rest of what is lingering in her mind. *What was that?*

Suddenly, she is standing in front of the Marriott, clinging to Dr. Jastreboff. She can't stop crying.

"Come on, Carol, let Dr. Jastreboff go home. It's late!"

"I know you want me to try to do everything I did before, but I'm too afraid. The fear is impossible to remove. I'll be stuck with it the rest of my life!" she cries, hugging Dr. Jastreboff. "You tell me that I register off your machinery for hyperacusis, yet I can't fully function in sound. A lot of noises still sound too loud and scary."

"You have phonophobia, which is the fear of sound," Dr. Jastreboff states.

Carol is hurt. Dr. Jastreboff hasn't meant to make her feel badly, but she knows he has told her she has a mental condition. She shouldn't feel terrible, though, because as usual, he's absolutely right!

She has been through a war of sorts. After what she has lived through and what still remains, she decides to go easy on herself. She knows her doctor would never tell her that she has phonophobia, if indeed she still had hyperacusis. If patients register low tolerance levels on his sound tests, they need to wear the generators longer, like Fred has to. Dr. Jastreboff wants sufferers to get well as quickly as possible. He is devoted to healing the afflicted.

She looks at the doctor she cherishes. *I must face this demon head on.* "How do I unload this phonophobia? Do you want me to see a psychiatrist again?" She is desperate to get well. She acknowledges her mental dysfunction.

"No!" Dr. Jastreboff adamantly states. "A psychiatrist will not be able to help you. You have to do this yourself! You do it little by little, like you throw a bone to a dog. It's a conditioning process. You'll be all right now," he says so full of confidence. "You can go swimming again!"

"I can? I can remove the generators? I can swim? For how long?"

"For three hours, if you want to!"

If I can swim for three minutes, I'll be doing great.

Carol kisses Dr. Jastreboff's cheek. She hopes she hasn't soaked him again with her tears of happiness. She watches his car slowly disappear down the street. She misses him already. She knows that she will not see the Jastreboffs for a long time. She thinks of Tobi. Then she thinks of Peanut, and she starts to cry again in the lobby of the hotel. People look at her. She has to get used to the stares. She wears instruments in her ears to save her life. The man she has just kissed good-bye makes the probability of her future a strong one.

Carol visualizes her little Peanut, lost to her forever. She will never forget her life with Peanut. *"Stop! Peanut! Stop right now!"* Peanut looks up bewildered. She doesn't usually hear Carol scream. *What's up, Mom? What do you want me to do next?*

Carol thinks back to Peanut's training: *Peanut's going to try to get away with a little bit more next time before she stops. But if I condition her to stop, maybe eventually, she'll do it more easily without trying to think about what she's doing, or if she should be doing it. She will just function automatically. This is what I need to do. If a Peanut dog can do it, I sure as heck can! Dr. Jastreboff knows it can be done. Then so be it!*

"**I** sure wouldn't have a surgical procedure done at this ungodly hour right after a long plane flight," Fred says to his already nervous wife.

Carol tries to defend her decision to Fred. "The more tired I am, the less nervous I get. Being worn out and exhausted is actually a positive thing for me now." She is wasting her words. Fred can't understand why she is subjecting herself to this procedure on this very morning.

She is in the operating room. The doctor injects her arm. She becomes disoriented and groggy. But she can feel everything he is doing. The tool down her throat is being pushed around. It feels like a toy car moving in her chest.

She thinks the doctor says, "Everything looks fine." She struggles to open her eyes. The white coat is gone!

"Am I okay?" she asks the nurse leaning over her. "I need you to call my doctor."

"Your doctor just left!"

"No! My doctor is in Baltimore," she wants the nurse to understand. "He is my only doctor." She fails in her attempt to explain. *This nurse thinks I'm delirious!*

"Lie still now." The nurse wheels her out of the surgery room into a much larger room with a view. Carol can watch the nurses' station.

"Are you telling me the truth? Am I really okay? I have something down there that's serious, don't I?" *Boy, did the nurses on duty this morning get stuck with me! Where's Fred? Probably eating his second breakfast.*

"No, you don't. And to make you feel better, the other nurse just told me that your doctor in Baltimore has already been notified that everything is fine."

Carol walks apprehensively toward the swimming pool. *I'm just going to check it out. No one's forcing me.*

The weather is perfect for her experiment in sound. She feels chilled from nerves even though the temperature soars to 80 degrees. The Bay Area is having its last heat spell before winter. *It's now or never. It's been so long since I've been in a pool.* Her eyes tear as she recalls everything—how her condition exploded on a day much like today, on October 14, 1993. In a few months, it will be 1997. Her last swim was on October 13, 1993.

Her tinnitus is acute without the generators. Minus the hyperacusis, the generator noise has dropped from a loud outboard motor sound to a soft, barely audible, low level air-blowing tone. Now it actually comforts beneath the tinnitus.

It's painful to be without the generators. Carol is tempted to run back to her house to put them into her ears. Instead, she removes her sunglasses. She closes her eyes. The sun is so bright. . . .

She is playing the game again. She draws a Fear card. It reads, "Why suffer additionally? Who cares if you swim? Is this really necessary? Is this really worth the added pain?"

She crumples it up and throws it away. She draws again. She has what she wants, a Strength card. It reads, "No pain—no gain! Go out there and show 'em!"

She looks at the water. The pool looks so cool and inviting. Swimming and snow skiing are her favorite sports. She has been swimming since she could barely walk.

Carol doesn't want anyone to tell her that she is an excellent swimmer. She only wants to hear Dr. Jastreboff say one day, "You are an excellent patient." She has given him misery throughout her illness. She longs to redeem herself in his eyes. She hopes to regain confidence and pride, and she wants his praise.

She stands at the deep end of the pool. *This is easy. It'll be a piece of cake! I'll get to fax Dr. Jastreboff that I did it!* The splash reverberates considerably louder than she remembers. The water is fantastic. She feels strange, but in a good way. She had felt dead before she hit the water, but now she feels alive again. It's like she has never stopped swimming. Her whole ordeal has been a nightmare which she merely imagined.

Could I be dead? Am I looking down at myself swimming lap after lap? How can I ever explain this to anyone, let alone to the millions of people I want to reach and help by telling my story?

The bubbles sound like forced helium being pumped into the pool. She keeps swimming. She tells herself they are normal sounds. She is just not used to normal yet. It has taken her years to get back into the pool. She is not about to quickly stop swimming now! She keeps adding laps as another place, another time, comes to mind. She travels back again to the day of her accident. . . .

Carol swims out farther and farther. The water in the calm cove of Bermuda feels so wonderful. She has no fear. She knows no suffering. She has defied Fred to be in this particular water on this particular day. She has swum in bodies of water all over the world. So why am I doing this when Fred has asked me to come home? *Darkness creeps in. Death awaits.* **Crash! Boooom! Rrrrrrrr!** *The sirens roar.* "You were in the wrong place at the wrong time," *Dr. Jastreboff is saying.*

Carol snaps back to the present. She is still in the California swimming pool. She vows to hang on strong through the end of her generator program. She stops swimming. She's out of breath. She's out of condition. *I shouldn't be thinking back to the past so much. I have to get on with the present.* She is trembling. She has forced through the terror and pain cards stacked in the deck. She has to tell Dr. Jastreboff immediately. *I'm really recovering from this!* She grabs her sandals and towel and races back to her house.

"I did it!" she types. "I just swam ten laps in my pool. When I breathed in the water, the bubbles sounded awesome, but I loved my swim! I wish you both could have seen me. I'm part mermaid, you know. Tomorrow I'll go the whole length underwater just for you and your research! (ha) Love, Carol." Her now-quiet fax machine confirms her transmission.

Carol doesn't have to have her doctor's response. She already knows he is thrilled by her progress.

Chapter 36

The end of the year approaches. Carol sheds tears of gratitude as she observes how pretty the Christmas decorations are. Their power sources no longer shriek in her ears through the night. She is so thankful.

"Where've you been, Carol?" a neighbor on the street asks.

"I was busy dying. Now I've come back to life!" she giggles.

The continuous lowering of tinnitus volume she needs is not a joke. The tinnitus is still causing suffering and pain, but she is now determined, more than ever, to conquer it.

"The quicker you can refocus your attention on other things, the faster you will recover completely," Dr. Jastreboff tells her repeatedly.

"Do you want to go to the health club that you used to love?" Fred asks. "You can rejoin, if you think you'd like to." Carol is speechless. At home, she swims in a small pool. But an Olympic-size pool, Jacuzzis gurgling in the huge locker room, hair dryers, exercise equipment, lots of people. Can Fred possibly think Carol can subject herself to all that noise? He does. Doesn't anyone know she's still traumatized? Dr. Jastreboff does.

"Do it little by little, like you would throw a bone to a dog." Dr. Jastreboff's words keep replaying in her mind.

"I will only try!" She firmly announces, her now favorite expression indicative of her condition. She is angry at Fred because he still doesn't acknowledge her "fear status."

"Please don't sign me up until I definitely know I can function here," she tells the health club membership chairman. No one, of course, listens to her. Fred signs her up.

When she protests, he says, "I have confidence in you!"

Carol is disoriented in the locker room. Everyone goes about their business so easily, so fluently. *Who would understand what this kind of trauma feels like? Fred obviously can't! It's no more real than hyperacusis seems.*

She has memorized her locker combination a hundred times. She mustn't forget it. Her life depends on the generators. She writes the code on the back of her lock, taking a chance no one will notice.

The swimming pool has gotten longer! She fights to swim a lap. Carol's swimming ability fights her trauma of being in sound. She forces a second lap, and then a third. "Are you having fun yet?" Fred asks from the next lane.

"Oh, yes! Thanks for having confidence in me!" But everything needs to be done quickly. She isn't able to relax just yet. She is still greatly afraid of the superpower she has had for such a long time. *You will not magnify anymore. You do not have hyperacusis anymore. It's over!*

"When will this terror go away?" she asks God.

"It is already changing. You are in the process of making it happen!" she knows is His answer.

Carol stares in horror at the bar of soap lying on the locker room shower floor. It has slipped from her shaking hand. She needs to bathe faster. She needs to get out of here and go home. She needs a safety zone to cower in. There is none here, or anyplace.

"I need some stuff in Longs," Fred announces. "Do you want to come in with me?"

Carol feels apprehensive. "I'll try!" Her pat response is programmed into her brain along with the generator sound that is bringing back her life.

Fred exits the health club so confidently, while she runs through the door like a frightened deer.

The store seems exciting. *A drugstore can be exciting?* She laughs at the thought. Everything says, "Buy me. Take me home." She has not purchased her own necessities for years. She cries over this thought. She doesn't care that people stare, wondering, "What's your problem?"

"**I**'m so happy you're getting back to all aspects of life. This is very important for you. Swimming is so healthy, and lots of fun, too!" Dr. Jastreboff e-mails.

Carol loves his letters. She continues to tape them around her bed in the far corner of the house. Pretty soon, the room will be fully wallpapered. His letters are her inspiration. They encourage her to try additional things.

She drives across the bridge to meet Arabella. She walks in the cosmopolitan City by the Bay that she loves, fighting hard to overcome her fear. She meets Arabella for the very first time. With tears in her eyes, Carol hugs her across-the-bay telephone friend. For months and months, Arabella had endured Carol's screams of torture. She has encouraged her to live through the most painful part of Dr. Jastreboff's treatment, the reversal of hyperacusis. Carol will never forget her kindness and support.

On the phone the following week with Arabella, Carol says, "You dooo? Oh, my gosh, what a coincidence! That's my birthdate!" Arabella has an appointment with Dr. Jastreboff on Carol's birthday. *Am I jealous? You bet!* Carol wants to be in Baltimore, too, on that date. She wants to spend her birthday with the Jastreboffs. "It is really apropos, don't you think?" she asks everyone who will listen.

"Can I go to Baltimore with you?" Norina wants to know.

"You didn't believe me when I told you a long time ago that I had finally found the only doctor in the world with the correct treatment, did you?" Carol isn't sure she wants to share her doctor. *It's my birthday, and he's "my" doctor. God help me! I really don't want to share the Jastreboffs! My father would spank me!*

"I knew you were sick," Norina goes on.

She's just saying that so I'll take her.

"Now, my God! You're doing things I can't even do. I'm amazed! If he can help you, then he most surely can help me!" Norina has made a good point.

Carol's mind relives her most recent feat. *She and David are seated in the Oakland Coliseum. Carol has always loved baseball! It's opening night for the Oakland A's. "What are those things on the field?" she asks her son. Before he can answer, she hears explosions ripping through the sound barrier, amidst 43,000 people in attendance. "Fireworks? I'm sitting here in fireworks!" she shrieks to David. "You sure are!" David says back. Carol is the only one in the crowd who is crying, crying with tears of joy, because she is able to listen to the explosions. She actually enjoys them. The fireworks are spectacular—so is Dr. Jastreboff.*

Norina is still talking. Carol realizes she has missed something Norina asked. Carol says, "I'm sorry, my mind wandered. It does that a lot lately. Well, Norina, I'm the living proof for the millions of people with any part of my horrible conditions. I'm a little walking miracle for medical science right here in the Bay Area."

"You most certainly are, Carol! I hope one day you'll drive up here and give a speech at my church. The other women don't believe the suffering I endure. They say, 'Gee, you look so great, Norina!'"

"That's because no one understands hyperacusis yet. But Norina, if I have anything to say about it, they sure will in the future."

"You never answered me, Carol. Will you help me? I need Dr. Jastreboff, too!"

So do a lot of people, Norina. A whole lot of them! I can't be possessive. And I can't be jealous. It's not nice. I have to share my doctor's knowledge with the world.

Carol finally says, "Yes, of course I'll help you. Not only will I help you, Norina, but I plan on helping as many people afflicted with this as I possibly can for the rest of my life!"

Chapter 37

"**A**re you really going to wear jeans today to the American Tinnitus Association meeting?" a surprised Fred asks.

"Why not?" Carol angrily responds. "I feel like making the same effort with my clothes as the misinformed doctors did with my medical condition!"

"I understand your feelings, but don't you want to look nice? You know most of the speakers."

"You're asking me to dress up for the doctors who nearly killed me?"

"No. I'm suggesting you dress up for yourself. Besides, just think how surprised people will be when you walk in looking so healthy now," Fred says.

"Remember, not so very long ago, I was the subject of a discussion between Dr. Jastreboff and the doctor who is speaking today. Not only was Dr. Jastreboff unable to convince him that I was recovering, this doctor had insisted that I was still his patient, not Dr. J's. Why would I still be his patient when he didn't understand my pain or believe me? He not only wouldn't believe me; he didn't even let me explain. He made it quite plain that he wouldn't bother with patients like me, just because I was hysterical. I wouldn't be standing here today if I had remained his patient. I would be decked out in whatever you think I should wear today—in my own little coffin, unless you'd have cremated me. Would you have done that, Fred?"

"My God, Carol! Come on! What was I supposed to do? I didn't know what was wrong with you or which way to turn. You kept screaming, 'Fred, help me!' all the time, not to mention waking me up at all hours of the night. I had to rely on your doctors knowing what they were talking about. I guess you're going to blame me for the rest of your life!"

"Who knows if I'll even have a rest of my life after what the doctors did to me! I guess they really don't know any better. They are evidently trained that there is no help or cure for tinnitus, and they know absolutely nothing about hyperacusis. But we know better now, don't we, Fred? Thanks to Dr. Jastreboff!" *Maybe I should let up on Fred? I sure rub it in enough!*

Carol goes to the closet to look for a more suitable outfit. The fuss over her dress code brings back other memories. . . . *It's so much like these jeans . . . for the ATA meeting. . . .* She remembers Fernando saying, *"That's awful! You're going with my family in that? Give it to Conchita (his maid)!" Everything I wear is, "Give it to Conchita."*

"Here. Try this on. My models all love it!" Fernando says, handing her a red leather dress. She turns it around, trying to figure out whether it is frontless or backless.

Carol recalls her ungrateful reply: "I'm not one of your models. Don't tell me what to wear!"

She tosses the garment he manufactures at him. He criticizes her selections too much! The dress lands on his head, covering him like the bright red lampshades she remembers seeing in Amsterdam. She doubles over with laughter. She can't stop giggling, because he looks so funny.

Carol comes back to the situation at hand. Her past thoughts are painful. Her present condition still includes horrible esophagus pain and tinnitus. *Thank goodness the hyperacusis is gone! No cure, huh?*

"All right! You win! I changed. How do you like this?" She twirls around and bows for Fred.

"Now you look wonderful!"

"Don't worry. I promise to behave!"

He kisses her good-bye. "Drive carefully."

She still drives with trauma, since she still functions with trauma. She knows what else motivates her actions: Revenge! She wonders what comes first, revenge or her love for the Jastreboffs. On this day, Carol has trouble deciding which is the stronger motivation for the game her life has turned into.

Tears well up in her eyes as she turns into the Berkeley Marriott's parking lot. The last time she was here, she was healthy and so happy, attending her high school reunion. *You danced so many times with Gordon. Now you're telling me that you're too tired to dance with me?* Fred had said, very annoyed. *Had I been so horrible that I deserved these afflictions? Does anyone?*

She notices that many people are already seated in the large banquet room. She is in exactly the same room where she had laughed and danced years earlier. She glances down at her name tag. She carries a notebook. People are staring at her and wondering which newspaper she writes for.

She sits in front of the panel of speakers, many of whom she knows. Carol has a pretty good idea what they will say, but she prays that this time she will be wrong!

She looks at the doctor whom she recently told she was better from wearing the generators. He notices her and seems embarrassed by her presence. He appears to be avoiding her stares. She watches only him. He says to the doctor on his left, "That's Carol Brook, right there!"

The audacity! She remembers her conversation with Dr. Jastreboff. "He didn't believe you about me, did he?"

"No!" Dr. Jastreboff had responded. "I wasn't going to stand there and argue. You can call and tell him how you are doing," he had suggested. She had wondered if this meant a lot to her doctor at the time.

She hadn't wanted to tell any of the doctors she was recovering. She hated them all. Finally, her conscience had gotten the better of her. She recalls this doctor's unwillingness to believe, as she continues to look at him in front of her now. At that time, he had said, "It's great that you're better. And what do you think made you better?"

Carol had been astounded. This was the very doctor who had ordered her generators, per specific instructions from Dr. Jastreboff. Hadn't he been able to see that she was barely alive at the time she came to see him? Now he's asking what made her better?

She had felt like replying with something ridiculous and sarcastic like, "I ate a banana split with three different flavors of ice cream. I like caramel topping the best, but I settled for chocolate," but she had decided against it.

Instead, she had said, sincerely, "Why, the generators are making me well, of course!"

"Oh, really? Are they? How do you know that?" he had asked with disbelief.

"Because, as a result of wearing them day and night, I'm able to function much better than I could when you last saw me," Carol testily had informed him.

"I'll have to think some more about this. I have a call waiting, so I have to say good-bye now." The doctor appeared to be uncomfortable after what she had related to him. She heard the click of the phone ending the conversation.

She had thought to herself, *You do that. You think about what I just said. Think about the millions of sufferers who could be helped. Think about what so many unknowledgeable doctors are doing to not help them. And then be glad I didn't die so that I can try to help change this horrible injustice!*

During the opening introduction, she hears William Shatner's name mentioned. She personally knows that the actor has given a contribution to Dr. Jastreboff to advance his research. They announce that Mr. Shatner has gone in front of Congress to ask for tinnitus research funds. *It's great that the seminar starts out with Mr. Shatner's caring efforts.*

Carol hears her doctor's name mentioned. The speaker tells about Dr. Jastreboff's research with noise exposure and hearing-loss studies. *That's wonderful, too! So far, so good.*

Suddenly, she is horrified! She hears a speaker say, "People with poor health have tinnitus two to three times more often than healthy people have it!" The speaker's words cut into Carol as if the doctors' needles were presently piercing her previously healthy body. She knows this allegation is untrue. Carol roughly estimates that this false statement has just been made to over one hundred and fifty people, including medical doctors and surgeons, at this seminar.

Linking poor health with tinnitus had caused her to try to make her own health better. She was forced to try to discover flaws in her perfectly healthy body. She was forced to diagnose herself because no doctor could do anything but tell her that she had tinnitus. She had started looking for anything and everything that could be causing her condition. She had allowed doctors to try experiments with anything and everything.

She had been so foolish, running to the poison center. She had weakened her exceptionally healthy body with hot sauna treatments. She had been instructed to inject serums into her system. She had let the doctors do intravenous treatments for no reason. When that failed, she had ingested megadoses of drugs to find relief. She had been so desperate, knowing that she was going to die unless she found the solution.

The mental ward was the last place she had belonged. Her outward emotions and actions had been caused by her afflictions. Unfortunately nobody, not even Fred, had been able to see that. The TMJ doctor had added additional pain onto a no longer endurable, rapidly progressing condition.

By the time Dr. Jastreboff arrived on the scene, Carol felt that she could no longer stay in the world. He struggled so hard to keep her alive. In her heart, she felt that he was far too late.

"Living is more than I can bear!" she would tell him. "Dying will be so much easier," she had tried to convince him.

"You have to be patient and try!" he would respond.

She had screamed out, "Just let me die!"

He wouldn't listen to her. But he made her listen to him! He made her believe in him, when all she had left was doubt.

Dr. Jastreboff is an honest and caring doctor who wants to help remove suffering in the world. His profession consists of sadness and struggle—sadness for the disbelief in his knowledge and treatment, and struggle in the too-slow process for change.

Today Carol sits with the generators working in her ears, listening to people on the panel speak against them. She is benefiting from the very treatment that the doctors are expounding ridiculous reasons against using. Dr. Jastreboff's scientific breakthrough has made it possible for her to be at this American Tinnitus Association meeting.

Here it is 1997, and people still do not know what to do to combat and overcome tinnitus and hyperacusis. *I'll show them when I'm a little better.*

She longs to stand up right now! She wants to shout out right now! "I had hyperacusis. I don't anymore! I had acute tinnitus, but the volume has substantially diminished. I expect to eventually not hear tinnitus at all. Tinnitus may not be able to be surgically removed from my auditory system, but if I don't hear it screeching through my ears, as far as I'm concerned, I am cured!"

Chapter 38

It's not time to speak out, but soon. . . .

In the meantime, she sits thinking of all the things she should say:

I have exceptionally low cholesterol. My family spent every summer at Lake Tahoe. I learned how to swim before I learned how to walk. I ski on the water, and I ski in the snow. I prefer to bike ride instead of riding in a car. I use sunscreen even though my husband says I look goopy.

I brush my teeth after every meal. I use dental floss, too! I drink filtered water. I have eliminated red meat from my diet. I eat over six fresh fruits and vegetables every day. I don't smoke or drink. Why, after all this good healthy living, did I get tinnitus and hyperacusis? It's not fair! Boy, I could sure knock down their poor health cause for tinnitus all in one fell swoop!

She remembers how futile it had been for so very long to try to persuade Jim to acknowledge that the auditory system is a separate issue from the rest of the body. Today she hears the ATA people speak like he had spoken.

Most people have something that isn't quite right with their bodies. Look at the odd chlorine and spandex reaction I had.

The doctor now speaking adds depression and anxiety to his list of causes for tinnitus. After this, she expects that no one on the panel will say anything that she will agree with. She stays only to help. She is convinced that she can.

The doctor who had issued her generators continues his talk. Thinking him very amusing, Carol starts to laugh. She wishes he were in the entertainment business instead of the medical field. He shows a cartoon. It illustrates a doctor ringing a cowbell into a patient's ear. She loves it. Maybe she will ask him for a copy of his cute cartoon. There, she has just found one beneficial thing from the seminar.

Another doctor recites many more causes for tinnitus. Carol writes fast, grateful for her shorthand skills. *Why is the doctor not mentioning a lunar eclipse as a cause?*

Still another professional speaks who mentions Dr. Jastreboff's habituation treatment. Carol strains to see his name tag. She notes that he is an MD. *Is anyone else furiously taking notes like I am?*

"On habituation," the medical doctor says, "I have to voice my negative response because of the twenty-four-month length of treatment time."

The fool! Some people have been needlessly suffering for more than thirty years. What's twenty-four months? Obviously he doesn't suffer from it. Carol doesn't hear which patient he has who requires the twenty-four months. *If I were his patient, I would need the generators much longer!*

Carol remembers one of the testimonials she had read in the ATA *Tinnitus Today* quarterly journal: "I had been suffering miserably with one shrill tinnitus tone. It was destroying me. After six months on the generators, I can barely hear the tone now, without using the generators anymore. It is amazing!"

Carol thinks back to her telephone conversation with the tinnitus sufferer. "You had one tone? Now it's gone after only six months?"

"Yes," the guy from Texas answered. "I was really despondent. I was just about ready to swallow a whole bottle of pills to end my life when my girlfriend ran across an article about Dr. Jastreboff's clinic."

"How long were you suffering?" Carol asks.

"Quite awhile," he answers.

"Do you mind telling me how long 'quite awhile' is?"

Carol is shocked by his response. "I was suffering four or five weeks. I couldn't have lasted much longer!"

"You were really lucky, then, to have found Dr. Jastreboff."

"I was lucky! I know it."

She thought of her incredible plight and medical condition. She cried as she wished him well and said good-bye. Carol was envious of the nice guy. He had found Dr. Jastreboff quickly. By the time she had, it was almost too late!

She looks with anger at the doctor speaking. *I'm learning from Dr. Jastreboff that every patient's medical condition is different. It's true, a patient can need twenty-four months or even longer, like me, with the generators. A time projection regarding habituation of tinnitus is impossible without test results and the proper evaluation of each individual. And then at the very best, projections can be speculative, as in my case.*

A short break is announced. Carol looks at her watch. There once was a time when she could hear the second hand ticking from quite a distance. *I want people to know what I have experienced,* her heart cries out.

The man on her left watches her. She looks up and smiles. She has been absorbed. She has not talked to her neighbors at the table. The man smiles back, "I came here to get help with my tinnitus. Now after listening to all of this, I don't know. I'm confused. Who's going to help me?"

"I am!" she tells him.

Carol leaves the banquet room. As she looks at the masking machine being advertised by the nice developer, tears come to her eyes. She slips on her jacket to walk out of the Marriott into sound. The tears flow forcefully now. She feels the warm, sunny breeze blowing her bangs. It's always windy by the water in Berkeley. It feels great!

264

She sees Albany Hill across the marina in the distance. It reminds her of the nine-year-old girl up there, on a windy day like this. . . .

"Are Indians really underneath this ground?" the little girl on the green bike asks her twelve-year-old brother.

"That's the legend, Carol. You better not tell Mom and Dad that I brought you here." He rides ahead on his blue-colored bike. They have been told repeatedly never to play on the hill. Carol hasn't obeyed. Soon the Indians will come and get her! She's crying at that thought.

Without warning, something bounces off her bike. She hears popping noises. She looks for the arrows. She's terrified! Her brother has stopped his bike far ahead. "Carol," he yells, cupping his mouth with his hands. "Quick, turn around! Go back! We're in danger!"

Carol's really scared! She doesn't understand how the Indians arrived so fast. They were hiding in the trees. Her brother pedals frantically toward her yelling, "They're shooting this way. Come on, let's get down, fast! Follow me!"

"Am I going to die?" she asks, as her brother approaches.

"No. You're not going to die!" Charlie answers.

"Am I going to die?" she has asked Dr. Jastreboff again and again—from May 1995 through May 1997.

"No. You're not going to die!" Dr. Jastreboff has patiently assured and reassured—from May 1995 through May 1997.

Carol looks closely at Albany Hill. Apartment buildings adorn her old Indian biking grounds.

"You'll only be injured, but you won't die!" Charlie had breathlessly said. "They're shooting BB's."

No Indians? No arrows?

Now tears wet her jacket from the pain of her brother's death. He had reassured his little sister with simply the facts—so long ago.

Carol had done what her brother had told her to do. In her young mind, she thought that Charlie had saved her life.

Today she does what her doctor tells her to do. In her adult mind, she knows darn well that Dr. Jastreboff really has saved her life.

Carol stands near the water, reliving her memories. *I hope somehow the deceased can understand what the living are experiencing.* She thinks of her family with such pain and sorrow. She thinks of the information at the seminar with similar pain and sorrow. She wipes her eyes and re-enters the hotel. "There's nothing more gratifying than helping others," her doctor tells her. *I'll try to help some of the afflicted individuals here today, Dr. Jastreboff.*

She walks out onto the patio. She looks at the food she cannot eat and turns around to leave. The doctor from the seminar says, "Hi, Carol. How are you?"

She pauses, contemplating her answer. She remembers Dr. Jastreboff's advice: "I find my best defense is a positive one."

She looks at the doctor who awaits her response. "I'm great! Really great! By the way, do you have a paper copy of the cartoon that you showed on the slide machine? I loved it!"

The doctor looks puzzled. "I don't know, but I'll try to find it!"

Carol tells the truth. She is great compared to her condition before wearing the generators. She will be even greater with more generator time through the oncoming months. And she really does love that cartoon!

The seminar divides into two groups: one for patients and one for professionals. A medical doctor at the front table smiles and pulls out a chair for Carol. "Why don't you sit here."

Does he think I'm a doctor? The seat looks like it's taken—a large tinnitus seminar text sits on the table.

Carol starts to get up. A nice-looking fellow says, "No, stay. I'm going to the other session." He grabs the tinnitus textbook. He puts plugs into his ears.

Earplugs = hyperacusis. I'll never forget! I'll talk to him later and help him!

Her attention turns to the speaker at the microphone. "Hello. Can everyone hear me?" The doctor explains about masking tinnitus along with taking the drug Xanax. He begins, "Masking tinnitus means to run a generator noise or other sound loud enough into your ears to cover up the unpleasant tinnitus sound."

Even if this is a less unpleasant sound to listen to, assuming you have only one sound, this method doesn't reduce tinnitus at all, Carol thinks, while the doctor explains the merits of this useless procedure.

He continues, "Studies have been done with Xanax that have proven this drug reduces tinnitus."

Carol knows how she would explain masking and Xanax if she were the speaker. She substitutes herself for the speaker on the podium:

"If a sufferer has hyperacusis, he would be in so much pain, he wouldn't be able to turn up sound loud enough to mask or cover tinnitus. Xanax is in the Benzodiazapine group. This is the same family of drugs that I have taken. The tranquilizers helped me stay alive with an impossible condition. They dulled my awareness of the situation. They kept me breathing through severe pain. But they did not reduce my level of sound torture, or give me any lasting relief. Besides, who wants to put a louder noise in your ear than the one that is already there?

"Of course I've heard—mind you, I've never tried it—that after masking tinnitus, when the sufferer takes off the masker, he may hear no tinnitus for a few minutes. Using me as a hypothetical subject without hyperacusis anymore (thanks to using Dr. Jastreboff's generator method), with the level and magnitude of my tinnitus, if this theory is indeed true, a few minutes of temporary relief would in no way compare to the permanent relief you get from wearing the generators and following Dr. Jastreboff's protocol. It would be lost in the shuffle of twenty-four hours of tinnitus torture a day. That is all! I thank you."

Then I would sit down feeling so happy! Would they applaud for me? Did I right this wrong?

Chapter 39

Another doctor, who is now speaking, uses a slide presentation. He is doing an excellent job of explaining Dr. Jastreboff's protocol. He shows Dr. Jastreboff's three categories of suffering. The doctor with the pointer says, "It makes much more sense to me to use Dr. Jastreboff's methods if one is going to use generators. A sufferer is better off working toward habituation to alleviate the conditions down the line, rather than just trying to control the suffering."

Carol agrees with his comments. Finally, a doctor who understands and acknowledges the absolute benefits of Dr. Jastreboff's methods! She is so thankful for Dr. Jastreboff. She is so proud to be his patient!

She is thrilled! This medical man has just shown the miraculous treatment for the auditory system coming from the most knowledgeable doctor in the world in this field. But her thrilled state is short-lived. In one split second, it turns to horror.

The doctor also expounds on the merits of other professionals practicing in this same area. "No one treatment works above all others." Carol copies his words verbatim. The medical doctor on her right looks at her notes and smiles. He thinks she is a doctor, too.

She wants to scream out, "There are no other doctors with any other treatments that work. I have died a thousand deaths from these afflictions! A couple of weeks later and I would not have been able to put even a whisper into my auditory system. I would have been forced to commit suicide like so many have already done."

Instead, she sits silently in sound. Her eyes are moist. The doctor next to her looks at her sympathetically. He seems to want to converse.

The noises in the room sound normal. The microphone is amplified comfortably. *I want to feel normal. I won't until I can successfully make an impact on people with my story, my true story!*

"Can you tell me the treatment for hyperacusis?" a timid voice inquires. Carol turns around. She wants to connect the voice with a face. She can't see way in the back of the dark room.

The doctor at the podium answers, "I really don't know anything about hyperacusis. Does anyone here know?"

Carol has a split second to act. She raises her hand and says, "A gain in the auditory system is called 'hyperacusis.' Dr. Jastreboff's habituation treatment reverses this gain."

"That's exactly right!" the doctor says to Carol.

I already know I'm right! She doesn't understand why this doctor didn't answer the question himself. Only the speaker and those at Carol's table hear her statement. She has not spoken through the microphone. She speaks only from her heart.

The MD on her right hands her his business card. She reads the tiny print under his name. He specializes in helping tinnitus sufferers. She gives him her husband's CPA card. She wishes she had her own business cards to hand out. The printing would read, "Expert Tinnitus and Hyperacusis Sufferer— Call Carol for Help and Referral for Cure."

Now that they have traded cards and are friends, she asks, "What treatment do you use to help sufferers with tinnitus?"

"I give my patients Chinese herbs and Xanax," the MD replies. "I check on them by phone. I make sure they are still alive!"

If this situation weren't so tragic, I would be laughing. She can tell that this doctor speaks in earnest. She really likes this man. He is kind. He is caring. And he seems interested in her theories. But he needs to be trained with Dr. Jastreboff's protocol.

A new speaker takes the podium. Carol knows this one, too. The doctor at her table and she whisper. Carol explains hyperacusis—how she was hearing things a thousand times as loud as normal. The doctor looks shocked. She writes the treatment in her notebook. She passes him what she writes. He reads it. He responds by writing down questions. She answers them in her notebook. He takes her notebook, reads, and writes more questions for her to answer. The doctor is smart. He is fascinated. He wants to learn from Carol's experiences. He believes her. He doesn't seem to mind that she is not even a doctor.

She writes Dr. Jastreboff's name and phone number down for him. He thanks her profusely. Suddenly, Carol and this doctor are back in kindergarten. They listen in astonishment as they are reprimanded. "You two must not talk! You two are being very rude!"

Carol gives the doctor a big hug. He gives her many thanks. She leaves the doctor, the room, and the physicians' session. She feels good that she has helped him. She hopes that as a result he will help many others. Now she wants to evaluate the patient-session room.

Carol enters this section of the seminar. She sees the nice-looking fellow with the tinnitus book. He's still wearing earplugs. A speaker is talking about acupuncture. Carol tiptoes over and kneels on the floor next to the good-looking guy.

"You don't have to wear earplugs anymore! Here is the name of my doctor who has the correct and only treatment." She writes on his notepad, "Dr. Pawel J. Jastreboff." She gives him the phone number, too.

"You're kidding! How do you know this?"

"Trust me. I know!" He looks so happy. *Have I made his day? Or maybe even his life?* "Now where's that person who asked what hyperacusis is?"

He points across the room. "That girl with the dark hair." Carol remains kneeling, waiting for the speaker to break. "I'm a musician. I have my own band. We cut records. But I can no longer work. Thanks a lot! I'll send you a record," he promises.

Carol scribbles her name and telephone number. *Boy, do I love being able to talk and walk in sound. All these men I've missed talking to!* She laughs at her passing thought. She has work left to do.

"I better hurry to catch her," she tells her musician friend, and says good-bye. The speaker has finished. The seminar is over. Carol darts across the room.

"Are you the one who asked about hyperacusis?" She is breathless from running over to grab the question asker.

"Yes. Actually we both want to know if there is any help for us," the young girl replies, pointing to an older woman standing next to her.

The other one pipes in, "I have suffered and cried for the past twenty-seven years! I drive my wonderful husband absolutely crazy!"

Carol immediately picks up on the "wonderful husband" statement. *That's really nice!*

Both women show Carol their earplugs. They both understand that they have tinnitus and hyperacusis at a functional but limiting level by using earplugs.

"Did you learn anything from this section of the seminar?" Carol wants to know. She needs to corroborate that she interpreted the same as others.

"No, not really." They both chime in like a duet.

"I was next door," Carol explains. "I couldn't be in two places at the same time. I wanted to hear what the doctors had to say. I just can't believe this!" Carol vents her anger and frustration. "You both sat through the whole gorgeous day here and you really don't know anything more now than when you walked in at eight o'clock in the morning."

The two of them look at her amazed. She knows they're thinking, "Who *is* she? She is awfully bold to chastise women she doesn't know."

Carol is immediately back in her ninth-grade English class. The teacher threatens the whole group. "You have all failed! I could give you all F's quite easily. Be thankful I'm only giving you more reading to do!" the strict teacher declares.

These sufferers are students who need to find answers. She again writes down Dr. Jastreboff's name and phone number. "Can we have your number, too?" they ask. She gives it to them.

Carol needs to clarify something important from one of the medical doctors who has spoken. She sees him packing to leave and walks over. "I understand you used Dr. Jastreboff's generators for your own tinnitus."

"Yes, I did."

She notices he no longer wears them.

"Was I correct in understanding, then, that you would not place all of your patients into the habituation program and that you would also use masking and Xanax as a treatment?"

"Yes, that's correct. What's your name?"

"My name is Carol Brook. I'm Dr. Jastreboff's patient. I'm writing a book about my experiences and Dr. Jastreboff's methods. I want to help people!"

"What did you say your name was again?"

"It's Carol . . . Lee . . . Brook," she says emphatically. "What are you basing your decision on regarding the generators and the masking of tinnitus?"

"I'll decide if my patients are candidates for habituation. If they are too emotionally overwrought, I'll have them mask and take Xanax."

Oh, my God! That's exactly how I was. This doctor is so wrong!

"So how many patients do you think will get the generators?"

"I would put at least forty percent of my patients on maskers with Xanax." Carol has heard enough. She is disgusted and horrified.

I would have fit perfectly into his high anxiety and stress group. I would have wound up permanently on Xanax and maskers until I committed suicide. Ruth would have, too! How many more would? I was overwrought. I was emotional and as hysterical as a patient could be. I wanted to die, to commit suicide. It doesn't get much worse than that!

With this medical doctor's theories, I would definitely have committed suicide. He would have placed me in maskers. He would have instructed me to turn the dial high enough to cover my tinnitus. My hyperacusis using this treatment and this medical doctor would have killed me—as a result.

There isn't a doctor here that understands the first thing about how debilitating hyperacusis is. In my case, this wouldn't have worked, considering mine was severe enough to not be able to tolerate even the sound of a pin dropping. I hate him, and all the others like him, because of their ignorance and egos! God help us all!

Carol prays that people, including the doctors, can be educated to understand the intricacies of these maladies, especially when tinnitus and hyperacusis are combined. She wants people to be convinced that Dr. Jastreboff has the only treatment that permanently alleviates these horrors. Everything else just results in some kind of temporary relief.

Carol is aggravated, but at least she has tried to help a few people. She visualizes Dr. Jastreboff smiling. Her day has been well spent. She walks out the same door she had entered for her high school reunion four years earlier. She's a very different person now. She has horrible medical experience and knowledge, but she wants to share all of it.

I'm so blessed and thankful to be alive. I'm grateful to have been able to attend today. I'll try not to cry, Dr. Jastreboff. Who knows what next year will bring? Maybe another high school reunion? My book will be finished for my former classmates to read. It will be on a table right outside the banquet room door. "Hi, Carol," one of my classmates will say. "You wrote all this? Why?"

I'll answer, "Because this is the horror that happened to me. And people need to have this knowledge!"

Chapter 40

Carol is now able to work with the generators in lots of good old sound. The more she is able to function and distract her mind with activities, the quicker the generators work. Her hyperacusis is completely gone. Now she feels the habituation process working on the tinnitus. She still hears some of the same sounds, but they are all becoming more distant and much lower in volume. She knows they will quiet down more and more with time. She hopes eventually to no longer hear anything from her agonizing affliction called "tinnitus."

She deliberately finds more things to do in plenty of noise. She is more determined than ever to hang on despite her remaining suffering. She struggles each day to unload her trauma. She still turns to the Jastreboffs for comfort and assurance. "Will my tinnitus reduce down to the point that it will not bother me, Dr. Jastreboff?"

"If I wasn't completely sure before, I am now. I'm positive it will!"

Carol believes him. She can't wait to visit him and his wife again. She hopes and prays and waits to eventually no longer hear any tinnitus.

She remembers the Baltimore collision man. She telephones the stranger's stomach doctor in Dr. Jastreboff's medical building. He tells her, "I can help you, but you should really try to locate a doctor in your own area. If you can't, I'll be happy to see you. In the meantime, double up on your stomach medicine. Who knows? Maybe it'll be healed by the time you return to Baltimore again."

The collision man had been right. His doctor was nice and compassionate. *But it's bad enough that Dr. Jastreboff is so far away. I need a local stomach doctor. Surely that's not too much to ask, is it, God?*

She visits Fred's longtime doctor. "Hi! I'm trying to live through something bad, really bad," she tells the intelligent MD. "I need your help."

He reads Dr. Jastreboff's "Instrumentation and Tinnitus: A Neurophysiological Approach." The smart internist replies, "I think eventually you'll be fine." He is kind. She trusts his knowledge. He refers her to a gastrointestinal specialist colleague of his. The two doctors will work together on her behalf.

I refuse to be a Humpty Dumpty with broken pieces!

Fred meets her in the gastrointestinal doctor's office. Carol can't hold back her tears. *What will this doctor think?* "I want my esophagus to heal."

This doctor doesn't say she needs a psychiatrist. Instead, he explains the functions of the multiple tablets he prescribes. Fred takes notes. Carol asks questions. The doctor appears to be conscientious. He wants to cover all the bases with his medicine. And he does, too!

Carol follows his instructions. She visits him for frequent consultations. Her esophagus gradually gets well. He predicts she eventually will be able to eat everything. *Guacamole and chiles rellenos. Yumm.*

On one of her monthly visits she asks her stomach doctor, "How would you have survived my condition?"

Her doctor looks sad. "I don't know. You're lucky to be alive." His sympathy is admirable. She will come to admit that she likes both her new gastrointestinal doctor and internist. They both are exceptionally understanding. She feels lucky to be under their good professional care.

At home, Carol finds a small package in her mailbox from Dr. Margaret Jastreboff. It's their family's favorite herbal treat. She receives it with much appreciation and love. She steeps the mixture in boiling water like a tea. She enjoys it, not only because it's her doctor's private recipe, but because it tastes delicious, too!

"I want to schedule some sessions with a dietitian," she tells her new internist's nurse.

"I can't approve that," the nurse replies.

Carol wonders if her fight to recover will ever be over. "I can approve it!" the smart internist says. And he does!

"You are too adorable to be a dietitian," Carol tells the young career girl. "You should be a model or a movie star." They laugh and talk. Carol learns that it's lots of fun seeing a dietitian, and very educational. Katrina lists the food groups. She expounds on nutrition for hours.

"I don't know what to eat. I'm afraid to eat because of the pain. I'd love to eat everything, but I can't figure out which foods give me this intense heartburn."

"If you can keep a record of everything you eat, I can help you determine that."

"You want me to write down everything in detail?" Carol groans at the mere thought of this cumbersome task.

"Yes," the dietitian firmly states. "Our goal is for you to be healthy while you're healing. It's important to cut down on the fat content in your diet and necessary to read the nutritional facts about each product."

She listens intently. She knows she now has two exceptionally smart local MDs. She adds the pretty dietitian to her smart list, too!

Carol stares at the sample foods on display. They look real. She is starving all the time. She wants to eat everything in sight. The samples are fake.

"I'll set you up with a nutritional, well-balanced diet, using the foods you enjoy."

"That's great!"

"I'm sure your digestive tract will be better in time. Here's my home phone number, in case you need to get me after hours." Carol is really surprised at her thoughtfulness. Katrina is conscientious and dedicated. Carol is grateful.

"Don't hesitate to call. I want you to check in with me at least once a week," Katrina instructs.

"I can't thank you enough."

"My thanks will be you getting well. If you can keep notes of what you eat, I'll have them as references for other patients with your problem."

"I'll do everything you suggest, Katrina." And she does, too!

Carol calls her dietitian regularly. She lists every morsel that she eats. She asks Katrina lots of food questions. She faithfully swallows all her stomach medicine. She finally has all the correct help and support which had been impossible to find for so long. She knows that her esophagus problem will eventually heal. Carol hugs her movie-star-looking dietitian good-bye.

Carol's life is gradually turning around. When she complains, "I'm still miserable with tinnitus sounds," Dr. Jastreboff responds immediately with amazing wisdom.

"When you're feeling bad about your situation, compare it with how it was before. Think back a year or more."

When she complains that she has to leave a mall because she is weary from tinnitus, he replies, "You can go wherever you want now. This is a very crucial point." His responses to her complaints always make everything easier. His words miraculously ease her suffering as she continues with his treatment program.

Dr. Margaret Jastreboff's counseling has the same effect.

"I can't stand the tinnitus!"

"Pick up your craft work to divert your attention," is one of her suggestions.

Sylvia is making stuffed animals. *Shall I try one, too?*

"I put his feet on backwards," Carol sadly admits.

"His ears should stand up," Fred analyzes. "And while you're at it, I'm not too crazy about his eyes!"

"Why should Fred care what the rabbit looks like?" Sylvia wants to know.

Can you believe all this, just for a rabbit?

"He's a very special rabbit," she explains to the crowd in the mailing department. No one seems to care. They only watch the rabbit. "He is going to the daughter of the doctor who saved my life!"

Carol needs to make them understand that this is not an ordinary rabbit and her doctor is not an ordinary doctor either. Now she has their attention. She proceeds. "I was very close to death. My doctor stayed with me from far away, just to make sure that I lived. I'm not an important person, but he sure is. He was on television, you know—CNN—with Mr. Ted Turner. Even William Shatner likes him. He wrote about my doctor in the May 1997 issue of *People* magazine."

"Gee!" they all say.

Now I've got 'em!

"Do you take orders? Do you do *Star Trek* figures? Can I buy this one right now?" a suspicious-looking man, whose wife carries a shopping bag, dares to ask.

"No! This rabbit is a one of a kind. He is to be the mascot for an important university back East," she explains to the couple who want to adopt the animal. "He's the only rabbit in the world wearing navy and orange. He was made especially for this important college student."

The crowd thickens. Carol grips the rabbit tighter. The crowd now is impressed. She is forced to watch the group closely for potential kidnappers at large.

Carol turns to the Jastreboffs for their wisdom. She treasures their advice. She feels their support clear across the United States, not far from where the rabbit now lives.

Celia and Lee are moving to Sonora. Carol will miss her good friend. She will remember all of the support Celia gave. *I promise to visit!*

Carol and Norina are going to Baltimore to see Dr. Jastreboff. Carol is sharing the Jastreboffs with her Calistoga telephone friend. *Isn't that nice of me?*

She and Fred wait for Norina in the Oakland Airport.

"Are you sure Norina knows what time your flight leaves?"

"I'm positive! I wish you were going with me!" She has promised Dr. Jastreboff that she'll forgive Fred. She will never promise to forget.

Carol feels funny traveling with someone she has yet to meet. But then, nothing connected with her condition has happened under usual circumstances.

"I'll be all right waiting alone. You better move the car or you'll get a ticket."

He kisses her good-bye. Two minutes later he's back. "I got that ticket," he mouths, holding up the evidence as he stands near the sliding doors to the airport.

Why am I not surprised?

"Have a wonderful time on your birthday!" he hollers in a final farewell.

She smiles as she thinks of the Jastreboffs on the opposite coast. Is that Chinese proverb really true? If someone saves your life, he is responsible for you forever?

"Is that you, Norina?" Carol laughs.

"It's me!" the woman responds. They hug. They walk, talking nonstop, toward the gate.

On the plane, "You talk as much as I do, Norina." Carol is outgoing. She always says what she feels. *Is Norina sensitive?*

"I know I do. I'm so excited! I get to meet Dr. Jastreboff personally, and on your birthday."

"Only because you are with me! Remember, it is *my* birthday. He is *my* very own doctor! I need to be able to talk to him as much as I want."

Boy, am I rotten! Norina doesn't seem to mind though.

"That's okay. I get very shy around important people. I think that what I have to say won't be that interesting. I'm just so grateful I get to see him. Don't worry, I promise I won't interfere with your conversation. I won't say anything. I'll be too nervous!"

She's going to do the opposite. I just know it! She's not capable of being quiet. Norina's gabby nature reminds Carol of someone she knows—herself!

Carol feels possessive. She doesn't want to share the Jastreboffs. *I'm being selfish.*

Dr. Jastreboff is more than just *her* doctor. Sometimes he gets one hundred and fifty e-mail messages a day. She is not the only sick patient in the world. So many sufferers seek his help that there need to be a hundred more Dr. Jastreboffs to heal the afflicted. The waiting list is long in Baltimore. For many, the wait seems endless.

Nevertheless Dr. Jastreboff is still my miracle doctor. He's brought me back from near death. I'll have to remind Norina of that often. Dr. Jastreboff will go out of his way, and far beyond his duties and responsibilities, to help anyone who's suffering with tinnitus and hyperacusis.

"I've been crying for so many years," Norina continues. "I can't get over how you're so much better now than I am. Look at you—the airplane noises don't even bother you anymore. I still have to sit here with earplugs."

It's not long before they are both laughing and enjoying each other's company. Norina is fun! Soon they will be having more fun sight-seeing back East. Carol has scheduled their time. She was almost completely unable to function during the last two visits. Now she's going to make up for it!

Carol and Norina like their room at the Marriott. Carol is no longer afraid of the hotel. They walk on the sidewalk to the Lexington Market. Carol doesn't remember her surroundings clearly. Hyperacusis will do that.

"Where's everyone going?" she asks two women standing near the curb as they wait for the light to change. She and Norina are being squished by a crowd.

The women look surprised. "They're coming from the baseball stadium," one answers. "The game just ended."

"Where's the stadium?" Carol asks excitedly. "When's the next game?"

"Why the stadium is right there!"

"Right where?"

"Across the street from the Marriott!"

"You're kidding!" Carol looks at Norina in disbelief. She can't understand how she could have overlooked the stadium. *The hotel room had windows? I was too afraid of sound to open the drapes. It seemed like prison before.*

"There'll be an even larger crowd tomorrow. It's Mother's Day."

Carol thanks the women and looks at Norina.

"I can't sit in all that sound, Carol."

"Well, I can now, thanks to God and Dr. Jastreboff! I'll be in that stadium tomorrow. I'll be doing my own scientific test on my little ears. Dr. Jastreboff tells me I could go in front of twenty jet engines. Can you picture me, Norina, standing on a runway yelling, 'These jet airplanes sound just fine!' as the planes run me over?"

Norina is astounded by Carol.

Chapter 41

Carol sits in the Orioles' stadium. It is May 12, 1997, four years after the start of her torture. She grips her purse tightly. She carries her spare generator, along with her story on a computer disk, which she can't wait to give to Dr. Jastreboff. The heat from the sun is sweltering. *Will the disk melt?*

She stands for the national anthem. The sound level is fine. Carol is overwhelmed. "You'll even be able to tolerate more sound than the average person because of my treatment. Your auditory system will get stronger from wearing the generators," Dr. Jastreboff has told her. "There are 47,451 fans here," the announcer says. "Happy Mother's Day!"

Her eyes are filled with tears of joy. *Am I going to keep crying from everything that I've missed?* She loves the Camden Yard Stadium, the most beautiful stadium she has ever seen. Baltimore is playing Seattle. The home team is good. The players are strong. She hopes they win the game. She hopes they win the pennant!

She feels the weight of her heavy leather jacket. *I need something lightweight for this heat.* She goes down the stairs and is directed to the souvenir shop.

Tortured by Sound

Carol now has very high level sound tolerance. She is no longer a weirdo. She is no longer inhuman. She is back to being a regular person, walking along a regular walkway, to a regular store. She will buy a regular Orioles' baseball jacket, and live a regular life.

The jackets seem large. She sees they are unisex. "Do you have a smaller size?" she asks. She wants to return to her seat. She wants to see the rest of the game. Buying a jacket takes a lot of time, she remembers from her life before.

Carol listens to the game from the televisions overhead. She is startled by what she hears. Everything in her arms slips to the floor. She stares up at the multiple television monitors on the wall. *Am I back in the halls of Albany High? No, of course not!*

She constantly relives the past, but why here, in Baltimore? She can't be doing this again! She is 3,000 miles from home. She is in the state where her wonderful doctor lives and works. Surely her mind is still intact.

She is the only one staring at the screens in shock. She looks around. Everyone is busy trying on clothes. No one else is paying close attention to what the announcer is saying. He is expounding on Ron Hansen, explaining the famous unassisted triple play that put him into the Hall of Fame. He mentions the year so long ago. *He actually is going on and on about Ron. He keeps repeating his name.*

Carol is standing in a gift shop in a baseball stadium in Baltimore. She is not standing in the school halls listening to the loudspeaker blare. But she is from Albany. She is testing sound. She is testing it with an activity of the highest level of accumulative decibels. This ballplayer being talked about was recruited from her high school in Albany, California. *My high school . . . the baseball souvenirs . . . it's a small, small world. . . .*

She makes a final research test in Baltimore using her enjoyment of baseball for the results. Ron Hansen had become famous with the Washington Senators. She is sure he made the team famous, too!

Carol wants to be the catalyst that puts hyperacusis on the map. She wants to help make Dr. Jastreboff famous. After all, his scientific discoveries will benefit humankind and the entire world!

283

Back in the stands, Carol admires her new jacket. It's really nice! She yells and cheers the Orioles on. She is just the same as the others now. She looks at the scoreboard. Her worries are over. *"You have made it through the crisis,"* she hears Dr. Jastreboff say.

The Orioles are winning! Carol is winning, too! The Orioles beat Seattle, 9-5. Carol beat tinnitus and hyperacusis!

Carol races back to the hotel room. She twirls around modeling her Oriole jacket and laughs. "Did you miss me, Norina?"

"I rested. I really needed to, but it's no fun staying in a hotel room all by yourself."

"Well, it's no fun staying out of the entire world all by yourself. People need to understand hyperacusis. I have to make this happen, Norina."

"I know you will! Just look at you!"

Carol laughs with her traveling buddy. "Let's get out of here, Norina. Don't you want to run around sight-seeing? I want to be able to describe something other than the medical building. This is my third time here!"

"I want to see something, too. I haven't had a vacation in years!"

I don't think anyone would want the kind of vacation I've been on—from life.

Carol and Norina leave the hotel room. Carol looks back. The door automatically slams shut. It closes without a hyperacusic sound. It also closes on a very painful part of Carol's life.

Carol and Norina grab a water taxi. They run all over. They ride two different trains. They use the metro system. "Isn't the White House gorgeous?" they exclaim.

"Smile!" Norina takes a picture of Carol in Annapolis, surrounded by a dozen male cadets in uniform. "How did you get all those handsome devils to pose with you?" people will later want to know.

"I told them they would be in my medical horror movie."

They tour the beautiful city of Baltimore.

"I left my camera on the tour bus," Carol frantically cries. "I can't walk anymore," they look at each other and say. "We can always swim," Carol adds, as they jump into the hotel pool.

"Yipes! Where's the heat?" Carol refuses to accept cold swimming pool water. Finally, the management is weary from Carol's perseverance. They fix it!

*I*t's *my birthday party!*

The Jastreboffs just came home. Dr. Jastreboff has given a lecture in Arizona. He is teaching his methods all over the states and the world. He has promised Carol that he and his wife would be home for her birthday. Here they are!

Carol talks to Dr. Margaret Jastreboff while she tries to digest some food. Norina talks to Dr. Jastreboff. Carol doesn't know how Norina can fit in eating. Other than for a hug and kiss, Carol has not been able to get a word in edgewise.

She looks over at Norina, then at Dr. Jastreboff. He looks very engrossed in Norina's Italian heritage. Carol has been to Italy, too. *No one cares! Do they realize that Milano is the fashion capital of Europe?*

Suddenly, her auditory system picks up her name. This is a perfect example of the habituation process. Carol's sitting right next to them, but she really doesn't know what's going on, except that she's going to kill Norina. That's for sure!

Dr. Jastreboff waves his hand toward Norina. He seems to be emphasizing a point, because she hears him say, "No, I don't have to worry about Carol at all anymore. She is gone—swoosh." Carol sees his hand wave her away in one quick movement. Dr. Jastreboff's hand swing reminds Carol of her backhand stroke with a tennis racket. "In five or six months she will be. . . ." His hand flicks again, demonstrating her exit.

But to where?

Carol looks across the table at her doctor. She tries to grasp the situation. She's missed her doctor's important message. She and Dr. Margaret Jastreboff discuss important issues, too. Carol will talk to Norina later. *You bet I will!*

Everyone looks at the beautiful pink cake. The French baker did a wonderful job on the heart-shape design. It's filled with strawberries and cream. She knows the Jastreboffs love the saying, "Thank you for giving me back my life." She sure loves the two of them!

The Jastreboffs have left. Carol and Norina remain in the restaurant.

"The food is so good here," Norina says. *She must have managed to eat something during all that talking.*

"It sure is! Fred and I didn't even know this restaurant was here. Not being able to walk around freely sure limits you. I barely made the whole first trip, and that was with wearing the headset. The second trip was so much better, but not like this time. I hope my digestive tract heals, so I can make it through the rest of this horror."

"You're sure making it now!" Norina responds.

"I ate a lot, but it's never enough. I'm always hungry, even though I have stomach pain."

"It will heal, Carol."

"I hope so, Norina. I think I'm getting too thin!"

"I wish I was."

"Not this way!"

Carol and Norina start to leave. Carol looks over at a nearby table. *What are those men eating? Pizza?* She is focused on food. She hasn't eaten pizza in years.

"Hello there, young ladies," the spokesman at the table speaks out.

"Hi!" Carol responds. "I was sort of looking at your food." She is half-embarrassed and half-laughing. *It is my birthday!*

"Do you want some pizza?" the man asks.

"Oh, no! No, thank you! I couldn't." *Of course you can! "Eat small quantities," the dietitian and gastrointestinal doctor instruct from California.* "I've eaten more than I should have." Carol fakes it.

"Where are you from?" the leader of the pack questions. "Is your husband here with you?"

He's sure nosey. Carol teases, "We're from another planet. The man who just left with his wife is a neuroscientist. He's doing research on the extraordinary powers that make it impossible for us to stay here. He's saving lives. He saved mine. I was dying."

"Are you available?" he asks, ignoring her technological glance into the future.

Norina nudges Carol. Carol looks at Norina, puzzled, then looks again at the man speaking. She tries once more, being serious, "I came here for a medical appointment."

The man disregards everything Carol has said. "But you're not with your husband, so you're free."

Free? Free for what?

"I'm the owner of this restaurant."

Is this supposed to impress me? I can't even eat!

Carol looks at this man. She is confused. She doesn't understand what he wants. She has been this inhuman creature from the black lagoon for the past four years. She wears instruments in her ears under the hat she now has on. She is struggling to regain her health. She has forgotten that there are other things besides sickness and death.

Norina pulls on Carol's arm and drags her out of the restaurant, laughing so hard she can't walk straight.

"That bozo! Wait until I tell Dr. Jastreboff." Norina starts to fall apart completely. The thought of her telling Dr. Jastreboff that he saved Carol's life for "Bozo" is more than she can bear!

"Norina, you're laughing so hard, you're going to drop *my* birthday cake!" Her silly friend can't stop.

"That old bozo was trying to pick you up!"

Carol looks at her friend. *I thought he was just acting silly, like me. This is evidently very very funny.* Norina is laughing so hard she can no longer walk straight.

"Give me that box, Norina, before you fall flat on your face!" *With my cake!*

Norina continues laughing. It's contagious. How can you walk down the street with someone cackling so hard and not laugh yourself? *"How can I walk down the street, Dr. Jastreboff?"* she had once cried.

Carol starts laughing. "Norina, now tell me exactly what Dr. Jastreboff said about me!"

"Oh, I just love Dr. Jastreboff! And Dr. Margaret is so pretty!"

"Nori-i-i-na! I know you love Dr. Jastreboff. I could tell! And Dr. Margaret Jastreboff is very smart as well as pretty. But where did that woman go who said, 'I promise I won't talk much at all to Dr. Jastreboff? I know it's your birthday.'"

Norina starts laughing even harder. Carol looks at her friend. *How can I be mad at her? I'm alive. I'm really alive!*

She cannot be annoyed with someone choking from laughter. In fact, she cannot keep a straight face bawling Norina out for talking nonstop at the dinner table.

Her friend stops in the middle of the street in front of the oncoming cars. She waves her hand outwardly, demonstrating. "Poof, and you're gone! See, Dr. Jastreboff waves you away. Five or six months from now, and you will be poof!" Norina loves waving her hand. Carol thinks Norina would love to wave her into oblivion so she can have Dr. Jastreboff all to herself.

Carol and Norina walk into the Marriott lobby laughing. Everyone behind the front desk stares at the two women. They are both acting completely obnoxious.

It sure feels good to be laughing instead of crying.

Chapter 42

The next morning, Carol enters Dr. Jastreboff's office. She sits down quietly to hear his explanations to Norina. She keeps her promise to help Norina. Carol has scheduled her own follow-up tests after Norina's. She is reminded of Dr. Jastreboff's long-standing advice by what she learns with her friend: "Every patient's case is different."

"I can hear now!" Norina tells Carol with tears of happiness in her eyes. "I didn't have the correct hearing aids all my life!"

"I can't believe that!" Carol is horrified.

"She was straining to hear," Dr. Jastreboff explains.

Carol is confused. She tries to understand. She promises to help Norina at home.

"Did I do the wrong thing?" Carol asks Dr. Jastreboff. She had arranged for Norina to be put into the generators without Dr. Jastreboff's testing, the year before.

"That was okay," Dr. Jastreboff says.

Carol sighs with relief. She knew in the beginning that Norina needed more than a generator setup long distance. She herself had been forced to do this to save her life. Her mind tries to absorb the fallacy of being your own doctor. Norina is an example of this misconception. She illustrates that. To put generators into your ears on your own is not conducive to recovering fully from these afflictions. She hears Dr. Jastreboff say, "Your friend is at the point where it's more beneficial to hear clearly."

Carol isn't sure she understands. Dr. Jastreboff is choosing hearing aids over the generators for her Baltimore companion. Norina should have had his skilled knowledge from the beginning, as Carol knew. She still feels responsible. She looks at the strong and willful woman with her. *I was just too sick to convince her,* she consoles herself into thinking.

Norina hadn't believed that Carol was recovering. She hadn't been debilitated like Carol was. She had finally become shocked when Carol was no longer home, confined to her bed, when she called. Norina had wanted to try the generators.

"You really need Dr. Jastreboff's expertise," Carol had said in the beginning.

"I can't go by myself to Baltimore. I have too much family responsibility!" Norina had replied.

Norina's hearing loss takes precedence over reducing her sound intolerance. If she cannot hear outside sounds, she will not be able to habituate her tinnitus. Her hyperacusic level will continually decrease with her renewed ability to be able to hear. Carol believes she has gotten all these facts correct.

"I love these new hearing aids. I'm hearing everything for the first time! I've missed everything around me for so long!" Norina beams with joy.

"I'm so glad for you!" Carol replies happily.

"I can't take the hearing aids home, though."

"Unfortunately, we need to keep this pair here," Dr. Jastreboff explains. "We'll give Norina's audiologist all the information. He can get them locally."

It occurs to Carol that Dr. Jastreboff might have to render her friend unconscious to get his hearing aids back.

"I want you to keep outside sounds around you at all times for the tinnitus. Carol will be doing the same thing."

"Don't I get to wear the generators anymore?" Norina asks.

"No." Dr. Jastreboff replies. "In your case, in about a year and a half, you should not be suffering anymore. You'll be okay. You'll have a better quality of life." He gets up. "I'll be right back to talk to Carol."

Her friend stays seated. She does not budge an inch. Carol gets annoyed.

"Nori-i-i-na! It's my turn now—with MY DOCTOR!"

She ignores Carol completely. Carol becomes more agitated. "I'd like you to please go back to the hotel, now!" Norina appears to be debating the issue. "I'll find out everything you are supposed to do. I told you I would help you!"

Norina reluctantly rises, slowly. She makes a funny face at Carol as she leaves the room. She moves behind Dr. Jastreboff, who is just coming in. To Carol's surprise, Norina sticks her tongue out, making sure she is behind their doctor—unseen!

Carol stifles her laughter. "I'm going to drown you in the pool!" she wants to yell down the hallway at Norina. Instead, she controls herself. "I thought she'd never leave!" she tells her wonderful doctor in Baltimore. "Boy, you sure made her happy! I told her what a genius you are!"

Dr. Jastreboff denies Carol's praise humbly. "I'm not a genius. I'm just a man, like any other."

Carol gets up and gives her doctor a little hug.

You saved me from a sure death! You've saved many others. I know you are a genius. Now I want the rest of the world to know! I want you to get a Nobel Prize for everything that you've accomplished and are still doing!

Dr. Jastreboff continues. "I could tell immediately what her problem was last night when she described the pain on the side of her head."

"She has worn so many different hearing aids," Carol confirms.

"This one will do the trick. It adjusts according to the environment she's in."

It sounds wonderful, like you are.

"There really are no sounds I can test you for that you wouldn't be able to tolerate. You already understand that you register off my equipment!" Carol doesn't know what to say.

Should she ask Dr. Jastreboff to add a higher pitch and louder sound to his machinery? She knows she would say, "That sound is fine, too!" More testing is pointless. Carol knows she'll never have to suffer from hearing anything too loud again. She's cured of hyperacusis. And her trauma is over. She looks at her doctor. Tears of joy shine in her eyes. She can never thank him enough!

"Will I be able to sleep in a quiet room again?" Even as she's questioning, she hears tinnitus sounds.

"Yes," Dr. Jastreboff quickly answers. His immediate response, so fast and confident, removes her remaining doubts. "If you use some of the environmental CDs, you can speed up your recovery. You have a chance of being one of my patients who will end up not hearing tinnitus at all, even if you try. We'll have to wait and see. You're in my best hearing category."

This is so amazing, but so is Dr. Jastreboff. But then Carol really worked hard to live. She hopes people understand that they can't put generators on by themselves and think they'll get well. The monitoring, counseling, instruction, and support for each individual are the factors that make this treatment successful.

Beware of any unauthorized person selling information on Dr. Jastreboff's methods! Alleviating suffering and saving lives is what this story is about.

I want everyone in the world to know that my doctor with his generator treatment can make it possible for suffering people to not have to listen to horrible tinnitus. I want them to know that tinnitus will still be there, but it won't be perceived and it won't have to be feared. The generators will retrain the auditory system to ignore the awful sounds. So it's the brain's perception of tinnitus that will be gone. Poof!

"Poof? A mild word to use for all my hard work!" the Faint Brain suddenly exclaims. "I'm strong! Told you so, remember? You've lost. I've won, you nasty Happy Brain! Now I'm the happy one! Tinnitus is out—Conquering is in! That's the goal of this game."

Carol's category is one with no hearing loss. *How can I have been stricken so severely, with perfectly normal hearing? I'll be quite content with not hearing tinnitus a majority of the time. If it is not at all, then I'll be thoroughly blessed.*

"I'd like you to complete my questionnaire," Dr. Jastreboff says.

I will never ever be on the charts . . . I did say that once upon a time, didn't I?

She knows all his questions. Now she has all the answers: "I have more than a seventy-five-percent reduction in the perception of tinnitus, as of today," she tells Dr. Jastreboff.

By the time I get to tell my story, I'll have a one-hundred-percent reduction of tinnitus and a full recovery. I will no longer need generators. I will have totally habituated tinnitus and will be completely well! Dr. Jastreboff agrees!

"The next time I see you, I plan on having no tinnitus." Carol tells the truth, sincerely believing that this will happen. And it does, too!

Carol has to move for the last time on the board game. She's close to the finish line now. It looks like she's going to win! She draws a work card. It reads, "Work to Succeed! You'll know when you win!"

She places the board in its box. Soon she will do the same with the generators. This game is no fun. This game is not easy. This game is called BEYOND HUMAN ENDURANCE.

"You do not have even a trace of hyperacusis. Your resistance to sound is better than ninety-nine percent of the general population," Pawel J. Jastreboff, Ph.D., her auditory genius, tells Carol.

"My tinnitus is reducing down lower and lower. Pretty soon, I won't hear anything," Carol tells her doctor . . . and everyone else who cares to listen.

CAROL WAS TORTURED BY SOUND.
CAROL LIVED BEYOND HUMAN ENDURANCE.

THERE IS PERMANENT RELIEF!
I AM THE PROOF!

Epilogue

"**W**hich of the sound discs are your favorites, Dr. Jastreboff?" Carol writes them down. "We're fighting sound with sound, right?"

"Precisely!"

Carol understands her doctor's protocol. She understands his **MEDICAL SCIENTIFIC BREAKTHROUGH FOR HUMANKIND.**

Carol can feel Dr. Jastreboff's lifetime of work and knowledge treating her auditory system. She understands how this is happening. She understands how she can make it happen quicker. She wants people to understand everything she does.

She will not waste one moment of this treatment by removing the generators until she is ready. She will keep inconsequential noises playing in every room of her house.

"Turn off those squawking crickets!"

We all know who says that by now, don't we?

Carol keeps her promises. She tries to be patient. She keeps her thoughts refocused away from tinnitus. She tries to help other sufferers. She does!

She waits until Dr. Jastreboff tells her that she can gradually wean herself off the generators. He does! She waits until he instructs her how. He does! She waits for the day when he says, "You are a good patient." And he does! She waits for the day he says, "Do not think of yourself as sick anymore." He sure does!

"Once you have reached the level of improvement that you have, it's only a matter of time for a full recovery. I was so happy to help you, even if I lost a few hairs doing it!"

Every night before she goes to sleep, Carol whispers, "Thank You, God, for Dr. Jastreboff."

P.S. Good-bye. I'm going skiing!

—Carol Lee Brook

INFORMATION FROM THE AUTHOR

In 1969, Dr. Pawel J. Jastreboff received a Master of Science degree in Electronic Engineering and a Master of Science in Biophysics in 1971 from the University of Warsaw, Poland. In 1973, he earned a Ph.D. in Neuroscience from the Polish Academy of Science and an Sc.D. from this same institution in 1982. His postdoctoral training was done at the University of Tokyo, Japan. He holds Visiting Professor appointments at Yale University School of Medicine and at University College, London, U.K.

In 1988, Dr. Jastreboff proposed a neurophysiological model of tinnitus and Tinnitus Retraining Therapy (TRT) while at Yale University. He also invented an animal model of tinnitus, which is used today to study mechanisms of tinnitus.

In 1990, he established the first tinnitus and hyperacusis center in the United States where TRT was implemented and is now being used throughout the world.

Dr. Jastreboff has also worked at the University of Maryland and is currently continuing his clinical and research activities with his wife, Dr. Margaret M. Jastreboff, at Emory University in Atlanta, Georgia.

For more information visit www.tinnitus-pjj.com or call (404) 778-3109. Courses teaching TRT are offered to professionals.

Readers may reach the author at:

Roaring Productions, Inc.
P.O. Box 2500
Alameda, CA 94501

www.roaringprod.com